The Aromantic Guide to Unlocking the Powerful Health & Rejuvenation Benefits of Vegetable Oils

Kolbjørn Borseth

Precaution

The information published here is not intended as a substitute for personal medical advice. Before making any decision regarding your personal health, please consult a GP, qualified aromatherapist, medical herbalist, other qualified health practitioner or a recommended reference book before using macerated herbal oils, vegetable oils, essential oils, absolutes, botanical CO_2 extracts and megadoses of vitamins. Pregnant women, the elderly, those with skin sensitivities or problems, or those with difficult medical conditions should be particularly careful when applying certain vegetable oils, macerated herbal oils, essential oils, absolutes, botanical CO_2 extracts, megadoses of vitamins and other raw materials externally. It's a good idea to let your GP, qualified aromatherapist or health practitioner know that you are considering the use of these raw materials as some may cross-react with conventional drugs you are or may be considering taking. Report any side effects to your personal health care practitioner.

Disclaimer

This information is provided for our customers and is obtained from a variety of sources, including the research, knowledge and experience of Kolbjorn Borseth. While we have obviously done our utmost to provide correct information, there may be errors.

USA: These statements have not been evaluated by the Food and Drug Administration (FDA). These products are not intended to diagnose, treat, cure, or prevent any disease.

Published by Aromantic Ltd.

17 Tytler Street, Forres, Moray, IV36 1EL, Scotland.
Tel: +44 (0)1309 696900 Fax: +44 (0)1309 696911
E-mail: info@aromantic.co.uk
Website: www.aromantic.co.uk

© Copyright 2008, Aromantic
ISBN No: 978-0-9554323-2-3

About the author

Originally from Norway, Kolbjørn Borseth is the founder of Aromantic Natural Skin Care and has been working with and developing natural skin, hair and body care products since he started his factory in Sweden in 1985. His passion is to reveal the secrets that the cosmetic industry would rather hide from us. He teaches others how to make their own products using natural raw materials tailor-made for their friends, family or clients. He does this by providing in-depth information about raw materials on his website, in recipe brochures, press articles, educational guides such as this one, and running educational courses. He is the author of *The Aromantic Guide to the use of Herbs in Skin, Hair and Health Care products* and *The Aromantic Guide to making your own Natural Skin, Hair and Body Care products.*

rewrite

Veg. oil book + Spa book.

Acknowledgements

As always, I would like to thank Finn Andersen of Crearome, Sweden, who started me out on this journey, when I attended one of his early courses in Stockholm in the mid-1980s.

My gratitude and fond affection to the late Lilly Johansson, with whom I worked for 10 years in Scandinavia, where she was a health icon. From her I learnt how to treat eczema, psoriasis and other skin problems.

Erling Urt from Denmark, who came over to London to teach my course participants about vegetable oils and who has expanded my knowledge about these valuable skin care materials as well as their combined use with megadoses of vitamins for effective skin cures.

My wife Helena, and my family, who are supportive in their understanding that for me teaching and sharing this knowledge is not a hobby, or even work…but a mission.

All of my loyal and hard-working colleagues at Aromantic who have always supported me, with special thanks to my 'right-hand', Monika Dachs.

Jacqui James, who helped me with the research on essential fatty acids.

Susan Kemp, thank you once again for your excellent research, editing, rewriting and proofreading work on this guide and my other publications. I know you're as excited about this one as I am.

Brenda Coverdale, Mike Harmon and Hassina Dadamya – thank you for all your help and support.

And last but not least, my customers. Many of you are my friends; all of you have inspired me to develop this knowledge further.

Introduction *Rewrite*

For many people, vegetable oils are simply something to have in the kitchen for cooking or perhaps used for massage as means of lubrication and as carrier oils for essential oils. In fact, most aromatherapists and massage therapists usually focus on the 2% of what goes onto the skin and into the bloodstream during a massage and don't pay much attention to the remaining 98%. The 2% being of course the essential oils, on which more and more legal restrictions are being placed, and the 98%, the vegetable oils.

To me, each oil is a rich source of potential, with unique and wide ranging healing, rejuvenating and otherwise beneficial properties. You could say that each oil has its own personality, which should be appreciated and applied appropriately.

Now, to move onto another important aspect of the book: language. We all know that languages are an important way to understand each other. I felt, in order to unlock the secret knowledge held by the 32 vegetable oils discussed in the book, that they deserved more classification than simply the fatty acid content. I have given you several new ways to classify, and a new language to understand, describe and use these golden treasures of nature more effectively. Further, these new classifications and descriptions will help you to use these oils synergistically, because just as with us human beings, you'll discover that oils with differing qualities are often the ones that work best together.

This is a book that I hope adds to your existing knowledge and experience, as well as deepening your appreciation and even more effective use of vegetable oils in a variety of products, whether for you, your family or your client's specific skin or hair type or condition. I encourage you to combine what you know with what you will learn in this book to develop and research your own recipes and formulas. However, for some of you just the joy of following the simple recipes and making useful products for you or others without any fuss or complicated equipment, will be very satisfying in itself. There are 212 recipes to choose from!

However you use this book, as with all of my other publications and educational efforts, my intention is for it to empower you to align yourself with nature by enjoying, and further unlocking the secrets of, her rich bounty.

Enjoy the adventure!

Kolbjørn Borseth

Contents

Vegetable Oils for Skin Care

Natural and plant-derived oils have been used by humankind through the ages for nourishment and medicine, as well as for skin and health care. Vegetable oils are generally extracted from nuts, seeds, and fruits. Extraction involving simple pressing in small oil presses has now largely been replaced by large industrial operations, which involve sophisticated methods and equipment and which now supply us, the shops and the cosmetics industry with these raw materials and nourishing ingredients.

Oils and fats have held a central place in human history for people all over the world, from so called 'primitive' tribes in the jungle to our own prehistoric ancestors or in the great cultures of antiquity such as those of Egypt, Greece, India, etc.

In all instances it has been natural for people to use fatty substances to moisturise dry hands after work or to protect them from the soil, water, plants, etc. Mixed with herbal extracts they have been used to heal damaged skin or as bases for aromatic or medicinal substances, not to forget the role they have played as beauty products for the rich and influential, the pharaohs, royalty, etc.

Naturally one had to use the fat sources to hand. These were vegetable or animal fats. The Indians in southern California or New Mexico, for instance, used jojoba oil, the Lapps used reindeer fat and the Eskimos whale and seal fat. northern Europeans used lard while in southern Europe, olive and almond oils were used. In India sesame oil was used and in Central Africa, shea butter and palm oil. Every culture and people in a geographical area have used the same fats and oils for the same kinds of purpose. They could be used on their own as cooking oils, skin care oils or as macerating oils to extract the valuable properties of herbs and plants. They might be saponified and used as soap or the fats and oils could be combined, heated and cooled to make ointments and balms. It was the shamans, medicine men and wise women of various cultures who began using fats and oils to extract herbs. Later monks, apothecarists and the like continued this practice.

During the last hundred years this has developed into its own branch within the pharmaceutical industry and it constitutes a large part of the beauty and skin care branch of the industry. In the period during which this giant industry has developed many of the traditional oils and fats have been removed and replaced by synthetic substances and mineral oils in more and more sophisticated products. Only a very few individual companies held onto the ideal of using the healthier vegetable oils and fats in their products.

However, during the last decade vegetable oils have experienced a comeback and are back in the limelight again, with small and large companies promoting natural botanical products.

Ways of producing Vegetable Oils

To gain a clear understanding of the different substances contained in fats and oils it is important to grasp certain principles. Oils are pressed from seeds and other parts of plants, which also contain many other substances apart from oil. These substances can be fat or water-soluble. All of these are substances that are some way chemically bonded with the oil. The fat-soluble substances that can be found in the oil after cold pressing are vitamins A, D and E, lecithin and carotene. The water-soluble substances are those such as glycerol (approximately 7-8% in all vegetable oils) and chlorophyll and can include substances like proteins and minerals. There are also traces, in quantities which are hardly measurable and therefore insignificant, of the water-soluble vitamins B and C. Some of these substances, such as lechitin, for example, are typically removed by filtration during the refining process. They would remain in the oil, however, if the oil had simply been cold pressed and not refined. When larger quantities of these substances occur they tend to sink to the bottom of the container that the oil is stored in.

There are several ways of producing vegetable oils:

Extraction using a Solvent

Seeds or nuts are crushed and mixed with a solvent (e.g. hexane) which 'draws out' the oil. The oil then undergoes several stages of refinement to remove the solvent and other ingredients present in the seeds or nuts. Heat is not necessary for the process. This is a very common method and is used to extract e.g. rapeseed oil. Yields a large quantity of oil. The extraction of oils from oily seeds and fruit is carried out in different ways depending on the raw material, how much oil is to be extracted, what the oil will be used for and how many impurities are present in the oil, and how many of these need to be extracted. By impurities I mean free fatty acids, wax, lecithin, sterols, mucilagenous proteins, fat-soluble flavourings and colourings such as carotene, chlorophyll, etc. The first step in extracting oils is to clean the raw material, getting rid of any dirt and grit. Then it is rolled or crushed.

Hot Pressing

Seeds, nuts and fruit pulp are crushed and heated and the oil pressed out. Hot pressing yields a larger quantity of oil but of lesser purity than e.g. cold pressing. The pulp left behind after cold pressing is often hot pressed to extract more oil. For hot pressing the raw material is heated to 60°C or, more often, to 100°C with a further increase in temperature occurring during pressing. Hot pressed oils usually have to be refined to extract the impurities, but this is not always the case.

Cold Pressing

Seeds, nuts and fruit pulp are crushed and pressed. Although external heat is not applied, heat is generated through the friction and pressure involved in the pressing. The raw material is placed in a press to which great pressure is applied and the oil is pressed out. This method results in less but finer oil of high quality, such as cold pressed jojoba, castor, sesame and virgin olive oils, to name a few. These are so pure that filtering them once is often all that is required before they can be used in food or for other purposes.

Cold pressed avocado oil is pressed from dried avocado, which results in a very strongly green coloured oil with a strong taste and smell. It is excellent both for use in food, and in skin care products, providing it is acceptable for these products to have the characteristic green colour. This oil is often further refined to produce a lighter, odourless oil. Personally, I prefer the cold pressed, green avocado oil and don't sell the refined type. Cold pressed, unrefined sunflower oil is often bitter and does not have a very pleasant taste. Because of this it is often further refined to produce better tasting oil that is used for the food industry.

Another way of removing strong tastes is to run the oil through active charcoal. The method adopted will depend on the quantity and type of impurity in the oil and, as mentioned, most hot pressed oils contain a lot of these. In addition to this, the food industry insists on oils that are clear, tasteless, odourless and nearly colourless and most of these are used for margarine and baking fat. So, I would not recommend that you buy most of the vegetable oils available in supermarkets for your skin care needs, as they are mostly very refined. This is suitable for cooking as refined oils generally have a higher smoking point than non-refined oils.

Refining

What is known as refining is a thorough cleansing of the oil, which can carried out as follows:

1) The oil is filtered through a filter or spun in a centrifuge.

2) The mucilage and waxes are removed by adding phosphorus, then the oil is rinsed with water and spun in a centrifuge.

3) Treating the oil with NaOH (sodium hydroxide, caustic soda) results in the removal of the free fatty acids, proteins and lecithin. The free fatty acids saponify and sink to the bottom and can be poured off together with the proteins and lecithin.

4) Colourings (e.g. carotene, chlorophyll) are removed by filtration through active charcoal or bleached earth, which absorb the colourings and which are themselves then removed by filtration.

5) Kieselguhr (a diatomaceous earth and form of silica composed of the siliceous shells of unicellular aquatic plants of microscopic size) is added, if required, to blanch the oil.

6) Any remaining taste or smell is removed by vacuum and steaming (at 150-200°C).

Solid refined fats are white and liquid refined fats or oils are colourless to slightly yellow. Both solid and liquid types are odourless and tasteless.

Hardening of Fats and Oils (Hydrogenation process)

The object of hardening is to alter the consistency of the fat or oil, to make it firmer, and to make the fat keep longer through transforming the duo- and polyunsaturated fatty acids into saturated fatty acids. Oils and fats are always refined before being hydrogenated.

Hardening is carried out by mixing a finely ground metal such as nickel into the oil. The metal acts as a catalyst to hasten the reaction and it is then removed by filtering the finished product. After that, liquid gas is pressed through the oil at certain temperatures and atmospheric pressures. Hydrogen atoms are added across the double bonds of the fat molecules, which then become one solid, saturated fat. Hardening is carried out with the fats used in margarine, baking and other foodstuffs, e.g. bread, biscuits, cakes, ice cream, cheese spreads, etc. Hardening can also done with oils, not to make them solid, but to make them thicker and to extend their shelf life. Hardening the monounsaturated fatty acid, oleic acid, and the duo- and polyunsaturated fatty acids, linoleic and linolenic acids, changes them each into stearic acid. Once changed, they lose their vitamin content and cannot be changed to prostaglandins by the body. This is how coconut fat is transformed into liquid fractionated coconut oil.

What happens to the Fats and Oils when they are applied to the skin?

Much of the knowledge already available is from traditional sources and experience and has stood the test of time. However, much research is currently being carried out in this area and we will certainly be hearing more about it in future. What is special about fatty substances compared with other substances used on the skin is that they penetrate the skin easily and are in no way 'foreign' to the body. The fats we have, for instance, just under the surface of the skin are chemically similar to the fats and oils that we eat.

Occlusives

The effects of a fatty substance will of course change as the fat penetrates into the skin. Its effect on the outer layer of the skin is that it forms a thin membrane on the outside of the skin and enhances the skin's own protective functioning without affecting the skin's ability to breathe. These fats protect the skin and body to a greater or lesser extent against the cold, water, wind, external irritants, chemicals and other substances that dry out the skin. They replace our own skin fats, soothing irritants in the skin and protect and warm us. These types of fats or oils are known as 'occlusives' and can be called a type of moisturiser as they prevent transepidermal water loss. A very good occlusive is jojoba oil due to the fact that it is actually a liquid wax, which will form a virtually invisible protective film of waxes over the skin.

The main occlusives are heavy, large-moleculed substances that sit on top of the skin so, therefore, oils that are rich in saturated fats are the main occlusives. Examples are: sesame, rice bran, avocado, pumpkin seed, macadamia nut, moringa, etc. Mineral oils are also occlusives, but they are too protective and so block the pores.

Different oils and fats stay on the surface of the skin for different lengths of time. Waxes are absorbed very slowly and provide more protection than oils. Fats penetrate deeper down into the surface layer of the skin and prevent drying out, helping to 'hold' the skin's moisture. One can say that a film of oil or fat holds the water back, preventing it from evaporating and as a result the skin acquires greater resistance to disease, is more supple, more elastic and softer. Certain oils, such as sesame, offer a certain amount of skin protection against sunlight.

What are Emollients and Moisturisers?

Emollients are substances that soften and soothe the skin. They are used to counteract or prevent dryness and scaling of the skin. They are key ingredients in many skin, hair and body care products.

Emollients are somewhat similar to occlusives as they mostly lie on the surface of the skin and so prevent transepidermal water loss. They also help to fill in surface cracks and fine lines of dry, dehydrated skin.

Fatty acids are good emollients, so all vegetable oils are more or less emollient. Emollients I wouldn't recommend are lanolin, mineral oils and silicones.

The terms 'moisturiser' (something that adds moisture) and 'emollient' (something that softens) are sometimes used interchangeably despite the fact that they really have different effects on the skin. Furthermore, 'emollient' is most often used to describe a single ingredient, whereas 'moisturiser' most often describes a finished product containing a number of ingredients.

Skin Nourishment

Oils that penetrate into the skin also carry with them the fat-soluble vitamins, sterols, carotenes, etc, which enhance the effects of the oil and also work their own effects on the skin. When the skin is nourished, warm and has good circulation it will absorb most of the fatty substances (from the layer of the skin immediately below the surface) and store them as deposits.

Essential fatty acids found in the vegetable oils are transformed into prostaglandins in the cells of the dermis, while the fatty acids are used in the cell membranes. If the skin is 'tired', cold, undernourished and smelly, with bad circulation, the oil with its high calorie content appears to be used by the skin to nourish the cells and to generate heat. Somehow circulation is affected, waste matter is carried away and the circulation of blood to and from the skin is improved. The skin regains its

vitality, colouring improves, sores heal more quickly and the skin maintains its heat more effectively. Healing occurs not only on the surface but also in the dermis, which is possibly thanks to the prostaglandins. See page 9 for information on prostaglandins.

Research also indicates that oils can be 'eaten' through the skin just as well as in the normal way through the mouth and that the body's essential fatty acid requirement can be met simply through applying for example, 15-20ml of sunflower, thistle, hemp, camelina or walnut oil onto the skin.

Without a doubt, oils and fats can be used as they are, for skin care and in skin care products but also for normal healthy skin where it is not just the 'beauty skin' which is being sought but also the fresh and healthy functioning of the skin, which will also ensure the quick and easy healing of any damage. This can of course be reinforced with exercise, fresh air, good diet and the use of botanical extracts, active raw materials and essential oils together with the vegetable oils. One very important factor when combating dry skin is drinking enough water every day. Approximately 2-3 litres a day depending on body weight is called for and remember that caffeinated tea and coffee don't count toward your water intake, but herbal tea does.

For the purpose of skin nourishment, it is necessary to select good quality vegetable oils and just as important to use the right oil on the skin. The oil should be suitable for the particular skin type and body part. Covering oneself with oil at all times so the skin shines like that of a bald head is not what good skin care is about.

When using oil on the skin it should always be massaged into or applied properly to the skin. Simply the massage itself contributes to improving the functioning of the skin. Care should be taken and the right oil chosen, especially if going out into the sun. Oils containing omega 3 (polyunsaturated fatty acids) oxidise more readily in and on warm skin exposed to strong sunlight i.e. when exposed simultaneously to their worst enemies, oxygen and ultraviolet light. If the oils oxidise in the skin, free radicals are formed which destroy the skin cells and make the skin go dry and wrinkle more quickly, reducing its ability to retain its natural moisture etc. Free radicals react with the fatty substances in the body's cellular walls oxidising these, so they go rancid and age the skin. The skins own oxidation process within the cell walls can also be hastened through the use of rancid fats on the skin. If using oils in the sun it is best to use oils such as sesame, almond, apricot, jojoba, avocado or shea butter (oil) and preferably with an added antioxidant such as undiluted vitamin E oil.

Freezing Point of Vegetable Oils

The freezing point of a vegetable oil is the temperature at which a vegetable oil crystallises, or changes from being liquid to being solid.

Melting Point of Fats

The melting point of a fat is the temperature which the fat or wax changes from solid to liquid.

Note: In this book, and for our purposes, I will talk only about the freezing points of vegetable oils and the melting points of fats. It is more complicated than this, but for the sake of clarity and keeping the information relevant to you, I have used this simplified system.

Saponification (SAP) value for cold process soap makers

The term 'saponification' is commonly used to refer to the reaction of a metallic alkali with fat or oil to produce soap. 'Saponifiable' substances are those that can be converted into soap, such as vegetable oils. The 'saponification value' given in the description of each oil is for the number of grams of caustic soda (lye) needed to saponify 1kg of oil to make bar soap.

Macerated Vegetable Oils

Dried or fresh plant material, usually a herb with medicinal benefits, is macerated by being steeped in a vegetable oil and agitated (shaken vigorously) daily for anything from several days to 6 weeks. The botanical material is then removed by filtering the oil, leaving the oil with some of the therapeutic constituents and properties of the botanical material, including traces of essential oils, and even the colour of the plant material.

Examples of macerated oils commonly available are St. John's wort oil, carrot oil, marigold oil, arnica oil, comfrey oil and others. Macerated oils should not be confused with essential oils or botanical CO_2 extracts. Most macerated oils contain extracts of plants in a vegetable oil base such as sunflower, sesame, olive, and jojoba oil. In the case of St. John's wort, chamomile, marigold and arnica the flowers are steeped in oil and the fat-soluble ingredients 'migrate' from the parts of the plant, such as flowers or leaves, to the oil. Typically carrot oil is made by mixing a base oil with various extracts of carrot. Similarly, calendula oil can be made by adding the highly concentrated calendula CO_2 extract to a base oil.

More about Essential Fatty Acids (Vitamin F)

Essential fatty acids are a very complex topic and research on these important nutrients is ongoing, so I am going to keep this as simple and relevant as possible.

The term essential fatty acid often refers to all of the omega 6 and omega 3 fatty acids. This is not medical terminology, but seems to have become common usage.

From a medical point of view, the term essential fatty acid refers to only two essential fatty acids, which act as building blocks from which all other omega 6 and omega 3 essential fatty acids are made in a healthy, well-functioning human body. They are linoleic acid, the shortest chain omega 6 fatty acid, from which gamma linolenic acid (GLA) is, and other omega 6 fatty acids are, made and alpha linolenic acid, quite commonly called linolenic acid, an omega 3 fatty acid, from which EPA and DHA are made. As the body cannot make these primary, or 'building block' essential fatty acids; it is essential to receive them through the skin or orally.

The two essential fatty acids were originally collectively called vitamin F, after being discovered as being essential nutrients in 1923. They were considered to be fats rather than vitamins but are still sometimes called vitamin F as they work in the same ways as vitamins would on the skin.

There is an indication that many skin problems may be caused by essential fatty acid deficiencies, for e.g. elderly people who have soft and sagging skin; or people who spend too much time in front of a computer and have thin, sensitive skin which does not circulate blood very well; or people who have large-pored skin (vitamin F reduces the size of pores) or eczema. Essential fatty acids are unsaturated fats and vegetable oils rich in these types of fat are used as emollients and thickening agents in cosmetics.

Notes of clarification

- In this book, I use the terms alpha linolenic acid and linolenic acid interchangeably.

- I use the term vitamin F interchangeably with the term essential fatty acids (in the medical sense). If I specifically want to refer to the individual primary essential fatty acids, I will call them by name i.e. linoleic acid (omega 6) or alpha linolenic acid (omega 3).

- Also, I distinguish between duo- and polyunsaturated fatty acids. Authoritative sources of information of vegetable oils don't always distinguish between these two and tend to group duo- and polyunsaturated fatty acids under the banner of polyunsaturated fatty acids.

- In the second section of the book there are diagrams showing the fatty acid content of each vegetable oil. The figures are the generally accepted maximum to be found in each vegetable oil. I have included the maximum amounts because the data I have researched can differ widely. The sources are all reputable, however their laboratory findings are different. In addition all oils, but the dry to very dry oils in particular, are subject to a variety of factors which may affect the fatty acid content greatly, such as geographical location of crops, soil conditions, weather differences and technical production methods and standards.

- I include this information so that you don't get confused when comparing the information in this book with other sources of information on vegetable oils.

Omega 3 Fatty Acids

Omega 3 fatty acids are a family of polyunsaturated fatty acids which have in common a carbon-carbon double bond in the omega 3 position; that is, the third carbon from the end of the fatty acid.

There are three main, nutritionally essential omega 3 fatty acids:

1) ALA (alpha linolenic acid), as mentioned before, is an essential fatty acid, which is found in dark green leafy vegetables, seeds, nuts, and a variety of vegetable oils

2) EPA (eicosopentaenoic acid), which is found in cold water fish oils

3) DHA (docosahexaeonoic acid), which is found in cold water fish oils

Although omega 3 fatty acids are grouped together like a family, their structural formulas are different. ALA, EPA and DHA each have unique cellular and molecular effects on the body.

There is some debate as to whether a human body is efficient at converting ALA to EPA and DHA. In general terms, vegetarians like to think that a healthy

human body can make the conversion, and so claim that a diet rich in alpha linolenic seed oil does not need fish oil. Those who support the use of fish oil sometimes will say that some groups of people cannot convert ALA to EPA and DHA efficiently, if at all, and so have to get their EPA and DHA from fish oil. The common theory is that people are taking far too much omega 6 in relation to omega 3 and this is affecting their ability to make the ALA to EPA conversion.

Historically, research has shown that this is correct, i.e. some research shows the body can only convert lower than 5% and other studies show this conversion level from ALA to EPA is as low as 2% from vegetarian food sources. If the body receives enough EPA, it will convert it quite effectively to DHA but, up until now, the only reliable source of significant amounts of EPA has been oily fish. But the good news for vegetarians is that there are recent reports of a totally vegetarian source of EPA in the form of an algae supplement. Research is also ongoing on testing the effectiveness of echium as another vegetarian source of EPA.

Omega 6 Fatty Acids

Omega 6 fatty acids are a family of duounsaturated fatty acids which have in common a carbon-carbon double bond in the omega 6 position; that is, the sixth carbon from the end of the fatty acid.

As mentioned before, linoleic acid, the shortest chain omega 6 fatty acid, is an essential fatty acid. A healthy body can use linoleic acid (omega 6 essential fatty acid) to produce gamma linolenic acid (GLA), which in turn is used to produce prostaglandins (see the next section for more information). Prostaglandins strengthen cell membranes and in doing so, the immune system. When not enough prostaglandins are produced, the skin becomes dry and wrinkled before its time. There is some research showing the topical application of linoleic acid to be effective in cell regulation, acne repair, skin-barrier repair, and moisture retention as well as being an antioxidant and an anti-inflammatory. [1234567] Because of these beneficial properties for the skin, linoleic acid or oils rich in the fatty acid are being added to more and more to beauty products.

Dietary linoleic acid is generally considered inflammatory. However, when taken internally with omega 3 (alpha linolenic acid) and GLA, there is an anti-inflammatory effect.

More about Gamma Linolenic Acid and Prostaglandins and their function in the body

Gamma Linolenic Acid (GLA)

Gamma linolenic acid is an omega 6 fatty acid that the human body is fully capable of producing for itself, under normal circumstances. The creation of GLA within the body begins with linoleic acid (LA), an essential fatty acid that we ingest in our daily diets. Generally, the body has a plentiful supply of linoleic acid since it is commonly found in almost all edible vegetable oils. Once inside the body, a key enzyme called delta-6-desaturase (D6D) acts upon linoleic acid, which biochemically converts LA into GLA.

Without this enzyme, the body would not be able to manufacture GLA, regardless of how much linoleic acid was present. Gamma linolenic acid is a duounsaturated fatty acid, and is the result of the body's first biochemical step in the transformation of the primary omega 6 essential fatty acid called linoleic acid into important prostaglandins.

Prostaglandins are essential to the proper functioning of each cell, while essential fatty acids formed from GLA are required for each cell's structure. Studies have shown that topically applied GLA has a positive impact on chronic dry skin and other skin conditions.

So, gamma linolenic acid is one step closer to the good prostaglandins than linoleic acid, as seen here in the GLA cascade:

Step 1 - linoleic acid

Step 2 - gamma linolenic acid (GLA)

Step 3 - dihogamma linolenic acid (DGHA)

Step 4 - prostaglandin E1 ('good' prostaglandin)

The process of converting linoleic acid into GLA can be very inefficient. If, for various reasons, linoleic acid is not converted to GLA this will result in a parallel cascade, known as the arachidonic acid cascade, which produces 'bad' prostaglandins and promotes inflammation in the body.

So, it follows that if linoleic acids are not transformed into gamma linolenic acids (GLAs), then a deficiency in the 'good' prostaglandins can occur. Many factors can trigger an enzyme to stop the GLA cascade from happening. To trigger the cascade you can take GLA-rich oils orally or apply them to your skin every day. The factors that can stop the GLA cascade are diabetes, vitamin and mineral deficiencies, pollution, extensive use of drugs, medicines and alcohol, as well as regular cigarette smoking and chemotherapy to name a few examples.

Prostaglandins

There is in the body a family of hormone-like chemical cellular messengers called prostaglandins. Found in every cell of the body, prostaglandins are responsible for control of inflammation, regulating water loss, body temperature, contraction of smooth muscle, dilation or constriction of blood vessels, passage of substances in and out of cells, and many other physiological functions. Proper balance of prostaglandins is a key to the health of the skin, particularly for quelling irritation, redness, and inflammation and for regulating water loss, and protecting skin cells from injury and damage.

There are 'good' prostaglandins, and 'bad' prostaglandins. The 'bad' prostaglandins are said to be manufactured by the body from saturated fat and increase inflammation and have detrimental effects on your body. The 'good' prostaglandins are generally considered beneficial to the skin and for reducing overall inflammation and are manufactured in the body from essential fatty acids and magnesium. It is important to recognise that the body's prostaglandins cannot be stored but must be constantly manufactured. By supplying the skin with a constant source of easily utilised gamma linolenic acid (GLA), oils rich in this essential fatty acid can help to maintain an optimal balance of prostaglandins in the skin. Borage oil has 20-24% GLA; evening primrose oil and echium seed oil CO_2 extract have 8-12%; hemp seed and blackcurrant seed oil CO_2 extract contain smaller quantities of GLA.

The skin needs prostaglandins and deficiencies will cause dryness, loss of suppleness and wrinkling. The skin will age more quickly and be less tolerant to sunlight and any damage to the skin will take longer to heal. Gamma linolenic acid is very well researched. Gamma linolenic acid has been shown to have favourable effects on a number of disorders. GLA-rich oils are taken internally to relieve premenstrual problems, alcohol withdrawal symptoms, high blood pressure, rheumatoid arthritis, hyperactivity in children, diabetes, itchy skin, atopical eczema (chronic, itching eczema) and multiple sclerosis. For babies it helps to treat their seborrhoea and armpit eczema.

GLA-rich oils penetrate down and into the skin, which as a result becomes softer and less prone to eczema and acne. They have a moisture-retaining effect, prevent drying of the skin, and increase the cells' ability to absorb oxygen and to withstand disease. Oils rich in GLA are not miracle cures but can help to support the body's own functioning to maintain good health. Borage oil is often used in preference to evening primrose oil as it is has a much higher average GLA level (up to 24%).

Examples and qualities of Vegetable Oils high in Essential Fatty Acids

Oils high in essential fatty acids are sunflower, grape seed, thistle, walnut, evening primrose, borage, hemp seed, rosehip, camelina and kiwi seed.

The qualities of oils rich in primary essential fatty acids (linoleic and alpha linolenic acids) for skin and body care:

- Thin oils that are absorbed fairly quickly by the skin.
- Drier than other fatty acids and so are very good for people with oily skin.
- Reduce the fattiness of other oils.
- Help to normalise dry, sagging or sensitive skin.
- Reduce the size of skin pores, so its essential to include them in products for treating large-pored skin.
- Essential in the effective treatment of eczema, psoriasis and acne-prone skin.

How to describe and classify a Vegetable Oil

There are many ways that we can describe a vegetable oil. In this section I will attempt to establish a new language that will make it easier for you to choose the most appropriate oil for your, or your client's, skin type or condition.

These are some of the ways that we can describe or classify oils, all of which are covered in greater detail.

Fattiness classification

Very Fatty Oils

These are oils rich in saturated fatty acids, e.g. moringa, neem

Very Fatty to Fatty Oils

Macadamia nut oil

Fatty Oils

These are rich in monounsaturated fatty acids, e.g. olive, sweet almond, apricot and peach kernel

Half-Fatty Oils

Avocado, jojoba

Half-Fatty to Half-Dry

Oils rich in both monounsaturated (omega 7&9) and duounsaturated fatty acids (omega 6), e.g. rice bran, sesame

Half-Dry to Dry

Oils rich in duounsaturated fatty acids (omega 6), e.g. walnut, thistle, grape seed

Dry to Very Dry

Oils rich in polyunsaturated fatty acids (omega 3) and GLA (omega 6), e.g. borage, rosehip, camelina, evening primrose

Very Dry to Very, Very Dry

Ois rich in polyunsaturated fatty acids (omega 3), e.g. hemp seed, kiwi seed

Smooth/Rough Classification

Oils that feel smooth when applied to your skin are generally fattier oils. Drier oils mostly have a rougher feeling when applied to the skin. The exceptions are rosehip oil, which is a dry yet smooth oil and kiwi seed oil, which is very dry, yet smooth oil. You don't need to avoid rough oils, but always blend them with smoother oils. Beware of using too many rough oils in products for sensitive skin or in baby products. Rosehip or kiwi seed oil are good choices for these products and skin types.

Smooth Oils

Sweet almond, apricot kernel, peach kernel, kiwi seed, macadamia nut, rosehip, coconut

Half-Smooth/Half-Rough Oils

Evening primrose

Rough Oils

Thistle, camelina, hemp seed, borage

Thick/Thin Classification

Thick oils generally contain a high quantity of saturated fatty acids and have a high viscosity, while very thin oils are generally high in polyunsaturated fatty acids (omega 3) and/or have a high GLA content, and have a low viscosity. The more viscous an oil is, the slower the skin absorption time. However, temperature can affect the viscosity of an oil. Any oil becomes less viscous with a rise in temperature. So, as happens in massage, warming the oil and the hands and applying the oil to a warm body will aid penetration.

Very Thick Oils

Neem, castor (high in omega 9 fatty acids)

Thick Oils

Olive, shea butter oil

Thin Oils

Jojoba, thistle

Very Thin Oils

Evening primrose, borage, camelina, kiwi seed

Sticky/Non-Sticky Classification

Solid fats are generally sticky on their own. However, when they are melted and then blended with other oils or products in small quantities, they are not sticky. Examples of pure fats that are sticky are shea butter, cocoa butter and lanolin (a type of wool fat that is extremely sticky). The classic sticky vegetable oil is castor oil. Because of its stickiness, you shouldn't use more than 10% in a blend. Generally the less fatty the vegetable oil, the less sticky it is.

Long/Short Oil Classification

The long/short classification is very important for massage oil blends. Long oils are oils that offer very good lubrication and spreadability qualities and have a long skin surface time i.e. 'one drop goes a long way'! The molecules of oils classified as long oils can stretch on the long surface area of a human body. Another good thing about using a majority of long oils in your massage oil blend is that you don't need to reapply the massage oil too often during the whole body massage. It is also important to remember to include a majority of long oils in massage lotions, which will be used for whole body massage. Doing so will ensure that you can massage the whole body with a smooth, gliding motion.

As a general rule, you can still use short oils in massage blends for whole body massage, but keep their content to a maximum of 30% of the overall blend.

For face oils or facial massage blends, you don't need to make long strokes to apply the oil so here it is quite appropriate to use short oils. They are also usually dry and so have the advantage of soaking into the skin fast, thereby not leaving an oil residue on the face.

Simple test for Long and Short Oils

To test for yourself how long or short an oil is have your oils ready. Take one drop of the first oil that you are testing and drop it onto a non-absorbing surface. Then 'pull' the drop of oil with your index finger, stretching it in a straight line as far as it will go. Measure and record the distance. Then repeat with the other oils. If you don't want to use a different finger for each oil that you are testing you will need to wash and dry your finger thoroughly before each new oil is tested.

Long Oils

Classic long oils are oils high in monounsaturated fatty acids. The longest of them all is jojoba. The exception to this is rosehip, which is dry as well as long. Other good long oils are sweet almond, apricot kernel, peach kernel, sesame, hazelnut, avocado, liquid fractionated coconut oil and olive.

Short Oils

Generally, very fatty and very dry oils tend to be short. Examples of very fatty short oils are castor and shea butter oil. Examples of very dry to very, very dry short oils are evening primrose, borage, and camelina. One exception to this rule is rosehip, which is long and dry.

Top/Middle/Base Note Classification

Using terminology from the perfume world, I have created a simple classification system that can also be used for vegetable oils.

A top note, as it relates to perfume/ aromatherapy terminology, tends to be very volatile and therefore evaporates from the perfume or aromatherapy blend before any of the other oils. Essential oils classified as being top note are citrus oils such as lemon and orange.

Middle notes consist of essential oils that give substance and heart to the blend or perfume e.g. lavender and rosemary.

Base notes consist of oils, which leave, or evaporate from, the skin and the perfume last. They give the perfume or blend weight and consistency. Base note oils bind the middle and top

notes so that they don't evaporate too quickly. They are usually distilled from roots, wood and bark, e.g. vetivert and sandalwood.

The way I've transferred this system to vegetable oils is not based on fragrance evaporation and volatility rates, but rather on the skin absorption times of the vegetable oils.

Top Note Vegetable Oils

Top note vegetable oils are dry, thin, volatile and active, which because of their low viscosity, are absorbed within minutes of application onto the skin. This takes a comparable time for top note essential oils to evaporate from your skin.

Top note vegetable oils are high in omega 6 and 3 essential fatty acids, such as walnut, borage, evening primrose, hemp seed, rosehip, camelina, kiwi seed.

Middle Note Vegetable Oils

Middle note vegetable oils are generally high in monounsaturated fatty acids (omega 7 & 9). They keep well for a long time i.e. they don't easily go rancid, and offer excellent lubrication properties. As middle note essential oils, these vegetable oils too offer substance to an oil blend. A middle note vegetable oil's skin absorption time is similar to, or even faster than, the evaporation time of a middle note essential oil, i.e. from 10 to 15 minutes.

Examples of middle note vegetable oils are rice bran, sweet almond, apricot kernel.

Base Note Vegetable Oils

Base note vegetable oils tend to be fatty oils with a high viscosity that give both weight and consistency to the blend, serving a similar function to base note essential oils in a perfume. Just as the base note essential oils are the last to evaporate or leave the skin, so the base note vegetable oils have the longest skin absorption time, between 15 and 60 minutes. They are durable oils that keep very well and offer excellent skin lubrication.

Examples of base note vegetable oils are shea butter oil, olive, macadamia nut, moringa, castor and neem.

When making perfumes or aromatherapy blends, it is important to use essential oils and fragrances from all three categories: top, middle and base notes to create harmony and balance in the blend.

The same applies to vegetable oils when adding them to oil blends or creams. The only exception is that you shouldn't use base note vegetable oils for oily, large-pored or acne-prone skin. This is because base note vegetable oils are fatty to very fatty and can enlarge or clog the pores.

Having said that, if you use at least one top, middle, and base note vegetable oil in your blends, you will ensure that your product contains omega 9, 6 and 3 fatty acids!

NB It's also very important to state that the skin absorption time is very much affected by your skin type and the condition of your skin. Dry, rough and scaly skin absorbs oil and the nutrition from the oil very slowly.

Rebalancing certain skin types using Vegetable Oils

I feel that this is an interesting and appropriate topic to work on for therapists serving people with special skin types such as oily skin, large-pored skin and acne-prone skin.

How is it possible to rebalance these skin types towards a more 'normal' skin type? A very important factor in answering this question is to work skilfully with the freezing points of vegetable oils and the melting points of fats that we put on the skin.

Rebalancing acne prone and oily skin

For example: we know that eating chocolate is not good for people who have acne or acne-prone skin. The majority of chocolate is made up of cocoa butter (in its purest state at least 50-60%), which has a melting point of 34-36°C. Dairy butter has a melting point of 32-35°C and other animal fats range from 30-45°C. Certainly, adding these foods to the diet puts an extra strain on acne-prone and oily skin.

By using more vegetable oils with a very low freezing point, we can help to counteract the problems caused by these fats.

Vegetable oils with a low freezing point are oils that are high in essential fatty acids (omega 6 & 3).

Before we get to the vegetable oils, we have to mention the various fish oils, which have very low freezing points of approximately -30°C and even down to -75°C (sharks' liver). You wouldn't use fish oils on the skin though!

By using the oils in the table below in your diet, you help to rebalance your body with essential fatty acids (omega 6 & 3) and you can use these oils in your skin care products as prescriptions.

Vegetable Oil	Freezing Point
Linseed/flaxseed oil	-25°C/-11°F (too volatile to use)
Hemp seed oil	under -20°C/-2°F
Kiwi seed oil	-20°C/-2°F
Camelina oil	-15 to 18°C/+5°F to -0.4°F
Rosehip oil	under -15°C/+5°F
Thistle oil	-10 to -20°C/+14°F to -2°F

Table 1: Freezing points of Oils that rebalance oily or acne-prone skin

Rebalancing large-pored skin types

Rebalancing large-pored skin is an entirely different matter as it is not based mainly on using oils with low freezing points, but on oils that contain high quantities of the essential fatty acids (omega 3 and 6) as they help to reduce the size of the pores.

The best oils for rebalancing large-pored skin would then be the ones shown in the table below.

You also have to take into account that camelina and hemp seed feel rough on the skin and so are the opposites of soft and smooth rosehip and kiwi seed oil. So, always add some rosehip or kiwi seed oil to the blend if using camelina and hemp seed oils. You can also take into account that vitamin E oil is very oily, but smooth and long. It is therefore good to use both for its antioxidant value but also to help to give body and lubricating properties to the blend as well as to balance the rougher oils with a smoother, softer feeling on the skin.

More about combination skin types

As the name indicates, 'combination' skin is really two skin types, and has a tendency to be oily in the T-zone. The rest of the face may have normal or even dry skin. (The T-zone is the part of your face consisting of the forehead, nose and the area around your mouth, including the chin. It is so named because it's shaped like the letter 'T'.)

Vegetable Oil	Essential Fatty Acid Content	
	Omega 6	Omega 3
Kiwi seed oil	15%	65%
Camelina oil	15-25%	35-42%
Rosehip oil	48%	25-36%
Hemp seed oil	55-80%	21-25%

Table 2: The fatty acid levels of the best Oils for rebalancing large-pored skin

Using Antioxidants to protect your skin and your products

We would all like to stay forever young and keep our skin like that of a newborn baby, but it is not possible. We can however reduce the skin's aging process, which starts as soon as we are born when the free radicals start the oxidation (destruction) process of all our connective tissues. We may slow this process by using antioxidants like rosemary antioxidant, which is a botanical CO_2 extract; and vitamins A, C & E. These antioxidants should not be confused with being preservatives as they do not preserve the products against bacteria and fungi. For that you need to use appropriate preservatives.

What are Antioxidants?

Antioxidants are substances that may protect cells from the damage caused by unstable molecules known as free radicals. Oxygen, an essential element for life, can create damaging by-products during normal cellular metabolism. Antioxidants counteract these cellular by-products, called free radicals, and bind with them before they can cause damage. When antioxidants perform this cellular repair, or transform the free radicals into non-damaging compounds, they are said to 'scavenge' the free radicals. This is why antioxidants are known as 'free radical scavengers'.

Normally, the body can handle free radicals, but if antioxidants are unavailable, or if the free-radical production becomes excessive, damage can occur. Of particular importance is that free radical damage accumulates with age and some studies suggest that free radical damage is the cause of aging. If left unchecked, free radicals may cause heart damage, cancer, cataracts, and a weak immune system.

Within the skin, free radicals damage cells found in the connective tissue such as elastin and collagen. Left untreated, this will cause wrinkles. By applying an antioxidant through the medium of a cream, lotion or vegetable oil blends on the skin every day, this damage can be halted. So, ideally, the best way to protect the skin from aging is to start applying antioxidants to the skin when we are children!

Environmental factors such as pollution, radiation from excessive sunbathing, cigarette smoke, herbicides and also many seemingly normal metabolic processes that involve oxygen from the atmosphere can also spawn free radicals.

Antioxidants are also important additives in cosmetic formulations for increasing their shelf life. The most noticeable changes caused by oxidation to products are the: loss of fine fragrance; destruction of vitamins and active ingredients; decrease of colour, especially of carotenoids; and development of rancidity. Sunlight and heat accelerate all of these effects.

Even with improved production methods, modern packaging materials and other techniques to help delay oxidation there is still the need for antioxidants driven by the demand for the ever-longer shelf life.

Oxidation is the same process that affects the skin, but it also affects cosmetic creams and vegetable oil blends as soon as they are made. In creams and oils, the free radicals start to "feed" on the oil molecules and the destruction eventually renders the products rancid.

Rosemary Antioxidant (Botanical CO_2 Extract)

INCI name: Rosmarinus officinalis L Extract $[CO_2]$

Rosemary leaves are well known for the essential oils derived from them, which are used in oral hygiene products, bath oils and massage preparations. However, they are also a source of highly active antioxidants belonging to the group of diterpene phenols. Rosemary antioxidant can be extracted by the very efficient supercritical CO_2 fluid extraction method. Rosemary botanical CO_2 extract is a natural antioxidant. See the section on botanical CO_2 extracts on page 21 for further information.

Antioxidants are important additives in cosmetic formulations for increasing their shelf life. The activity of rosemary diterpene phenols has been shown to retard the oxidation of lard. In all studies, the rosemary diterpene phenols have been active in low concentrations and could easily replace synthetic antioxidants.

Using Rosemary Antioxidant

Rosemary botanical CO_2 extract antioxidant is more stable than vitamin E for products such as creams and vegetable oil blends. When adding more

than 3% vitamin E oil to any blend, I recommend that you also add rosemary botanical CO_2 extract to protect the vitamin E oil from going rancid, as it is more stable than vitamin E oil.

To use Rosemary Antioxidant to slow the process of your products going rancid, follow these Dosage guidelines

- 0.02%-0.1% in products which contain mostly saturated fatty acids
- 0.2%-0.4% in products which contain mostly duo- and polyunsaturated fatty acids

Vitamin E

INCI name: Tocopherol

Vitamin E is the name given to several tocopherols of which alpha tocopherol is the most active. Alpha tocopherol can be produced chemically (dl-alpha-tocopherol) or be extracted from e.g. soy beans and sunflower. Natural vitamin E is more reactive than its chemically produced counterpart with the same vitamin content. 100%, undiluted vitamin E oil is very fatty and sticky and it needs to be blended with drier oils.

The tocopherols operate and are active both in the product and on the person's skin and inner organs. The need for tocopherols in products or in the human body will depend on the number and quantity of compounds prone to oxidisation such as polyunsaturated fatty acids (omega 3), which are present. The more polyunsaturated fat one eats, the more tocopherol one will need. Similarly the more polyunsaturated fatty acids in a product, the more tocopherol it will need to contain.

Tocopherols protect against the side effects of radiotherapy and cytotoxins. Free radicals are formed during exposure to sunlight, during the breaking down of environmental pollutants and during the oxidation of oils when exposed to heat or sunlight. Vitamin E applied to the skin will penetrate it and take care of the free radicals. The vitamin will absorb the sun's dangerous ultraviolet rays, which are responsible for the reddening of the skin, sunburn and more serious burns. Ultraviolet rays and the subsequently formed free radicals age the skin more quickly, reducing its elasticity and creating wrinkles. Vitamin E therefore works to prevent wrinkles, stimulates the blood circulation and regulates the skin's elasticity.

Hemp seed, evening primrose, borage, camelina and rosehip oils go rancid after 5-6 months and kiwi seed after 4-6 weeks without an added antioxidant such as vitamin E oil. Food-grade vitamin E oil is the easiest and safest to work with. Vitamin E oil acts as a barrier for the other ingredients in the product. The free radicals attack and start to feed on the most potent molecules in the blend (which in this case is vitamin E oil). The other ingredients are then safe.

This destruction of vitamin E oil can take 1.5–2.5 years. This same process occurs in the skin, but unfortunately you need to apply vitamin E oil every day to protect the skin effectively.

Dosage guidelines

Vitamin E Oil is recommended as a safe antioxidant. The smallest amount of vitamin E oil to use is 0.5%, which will prolong the shelf life to around 2 years. This quantity is sufficient to protect the product's ingredients but you will need to add much more to protect the shelf life of the skin! That is, to protect the skin tissue against free radical formation induced by UV-radiation and chemical environmental influences. For anti-wrinkle and skin protection you need to increase the amount of vitamin E oil from 2-3% up to 10-35% for oil blends and serums or increase it to 5-6% in creams.

Most commercial products do not contain enough vitamins to protect the skin in this way. You can use up to 50-60% of vitamin E oil in an oil blend and although very safe to use on the skin, it should never be taken internally at these levels. Applying 10-35% vitamin E oil keeps the skin in good condition and increases the growth of new skin cells. In this way, it works as a skin exfoliant as the old skin is exfoliated because of the boosting of the production of new cells under the top layer of these old skin cells. It also increases the circulation, so don't worry if your skin gets slightly reddish.

Vitamin E oil is a very oily substance so if you have oily skin you need to combine it with a high dosage of thin dry vegetable oil. When you make a cream or face oil you need only add the antioxidant (vitamin E oil) once to keep the product fresh. To work as an antioxidant for your skin you need to apply it every day.

Which is best to use: artificial or natural?

Generally I recommend using the artificial vitamin E for both extending the shelf life of products as well as for the purpose of an antioxidant on the skin as the artificial vitamin E becomes more active when put into a product compared with the natural vitamin E.

Natural vitamin E becomes more active in contact with the skin compared with the artificial vitamin E. I also reckon that the natural vitamin E has better healing properties on the skin than the artificial type.

So, you could put 50% of the natural and

50% of the artificial vitamin E into your products to get the optimal results for the product's shelf life as well as for the skin.

However, should cost or availability prohibit you from using the natural vitamin E, then I consider the artificial vitamin E to be a sufficiently active antioxidant for both the product and the skin.

When adding more than 5% of vitamin E, whether artificial or natural, to your products, I suggest that you always add an additional antioxidant e.g. rosemary CO_2 extract, to protect the vitamin E.

Vitamin A

INCI name: Retinol palmitate

Vitamin A, or retinol palmitate, is by itself a very dry oil and so it needs to be blended with fattier oils. It plays an important role in the functioning of the eyes and the making of new skin and mucous membranes. It prevents infections in the respiratory mucous membranes. Vitamin A occurs naturally in liver, fish oils and egg yolk (primarily as retinol). The daily recommended intake for adults is 2.500-5000 IU. Excess vitamin A is stored in the liver. With larger doses (50.000-100.000 IU per day) the liver is unable to store the excess and this is then spread around the body and can cause symptoms such as headache, hair loss, feeling unwell and fatigue.

It is important in natural skin care as vitamin A nourishes the skin, counteracts inflammations and acts as an antioxidant, protecting cell membranes and other structures within the cells from the damage caused by free radicals and in this way helps to prevent skin disorders.

Vitamin A is produced synthetically. Natural compounds can be used e.g. those found in betacarotene or essential oils. The skin absorbs retinyl palmitate and it is used in skin care products for dry, aging, lifeless skin, and in the treatment of acne, eczema and psoriasis. Vitamin A increases blood flow, stimulates the skin and protects against sunburn. Vitamin A is also used in anti-wrinkle creams, face oils and face serums where it is claimed to 'remove' wrinkles. Safe dosage for everyday use: 0.5-1%. Dosage for intensive skin care: up to 2%. **Note**: vitamin A should never be used in a dosage of over 2% if used daily.

Vitamin C

INCI name: Ascorbyl Phosphate

Vitamin C is essential for the formation of collagen. Insufficient vitamin C in the diet results in an inability to add hydroxyl groups to growing collagen fibres. In addition, the skin is the first line of defence against many environmental assaults. It is here that Vitamin C also serves as an antioxidant by scavenging free radicals. These are highly reactive chemical species that are generated in cells and tissues by sunlight, tobacco smoke and also many seemingly normal metabolic processes that involve oxygen from the atmosphere. These scavenging reactions deplete the level of vitamin C and so it makes sense to apply it topically to those areas where it can boost needed antioxidant protection. Dosage: 1-2% for serums; up to 10% in skin lighteners.

Note: Vitamin C powder cannot be used in oil blends, as it is water based and therefore cannot dissolve in oil. It is first dissolved in water and then added to water-based products or in the water stage of a recipe for creams, for example. Some large professional cosmetic companies use oil-based vitamin C but it's not available to smaller companies at the time of writing this book.

Botanical CO_2 Extracts

Handwritten annotations: bodymilk, Lotions & body oils, anti wrinkle serums, massage oils, lip balms, ointments and balms, shampoos and gels, soaps

You will find that botanical CO_2 extracts are often included in the recipes in this book, so here we have a quick look at what they are. *(C1)*

In the cosmetic field, CO_2 (carbon dioxide) extracts are used as bioactive components in creams, ~~skin oils, body milks and lotions~~, before and after sun products, etc. Supercritical CO_2 fluid extraction is an established process for the decaffeination of tea and coffee, as well as for hop ingredients, of perfumery and aromatherapy. CO_2 extracts are becoming more and more popular. The intention is to eliminate harmful organic solvents used in the past for the production of lipophilic (fat-loving) botanical extracts, to avoid environmental pollution and to have a high grade extract composition very close to the natural raw material.

The benefits of CO_2 extraction can be summarised as: *(C2)*

- less rearrangement of essential oil constituents because low temperature is used
- no concern regarding solvent residues
- CO_2 is acceptable as a food grade "solvent"
- low temperature processing means sensitive products do not deteriorate
- gentle extraction process
- high quality separation eliminates the need to remove solvent and other residues by further processing
- standardised extracts

- highly concentrated
- Compared to propylene glycolic extracts, where the solvent is retained in the botanical product (and thus must be declared as a component of the cosmetic formulation), the CO_2 extracts are much more pure and in a concentrated form. They are free of any solvent residues and diluting agents and are composed almost exclusively of the raw material's ingredients without any dilution and accordingly can be used in a fairly low dosage. This low dosage means that a high quality, active cosmetic product can be ~~created at a reduced~~ cost.

(C2)

Botanical CO_2 Extracts dosage guidelines

These botanical CO_2 extracts are generally used in a concentration of 1-2% in creams, lotions, ointments and vegetable oils, etc. They are easily dissolved into the product at temperatures under 40°C or can be simply added to your vegetable oils without heating. If you choose to use more than one CO_2 extract, know that the extracts are very concentrated in their effect and it's not necessary to have more than a total maximum amount of 5% extract in your product.

Handwritten annotations: 0.5-2% all cosmetic prod. *(C4)*

Botanical CO_2 Extracts found in the Recipes in this book

I haven't included the INCI names for any added vegetable oils or antioxidants.

Arctic Blackcurrant CO_2 Extract

INCI name: Ribes nigrum Extract [CO_2]

It is one of the few plant oils containing omega 6 and omega 3 fatty acids in an optimal physiological ratio and is an excellent, nourishing addition to all skin care products, especially skin rejuvenating products. Contains 2% stearidonic acid, which reduces skin inflammation by suppressing the release of arachidonic acid, amongst other cell activities.

Arctic Cranberry Seed Oil CO_2 Extract

INCI name: Oxycoccus palustris Extract [CO_2]

Arctic cranberry seed oil provides a high level of essential fatty acids and tocotrienols, offering a three-in-one kit for nourishing, moisturising and protecting the skin in the most natural way. It's excellent to use in facial and body oils, especially in anti-wrinkle and anti-aging blends.

Calendula CO_2 Extract

INCI name: Calendula officinalis Extract [CO_2]

Also known as marigold CO_2 extract. Well known for its healing properties and is often used on sensitive or inflamed skin.

Carrot CO_2 Extract

INCI name: Daucus carota Extract [CO_2]

Well known for its antioxidant properties.

Chamomile CO_2 Extract

INCI name: Matricaria chamomilla Extract [CO_2]

Well known for its calming and soothing properties.

Echium Seed Oil CO_2 Extract

INCI name: Echium plantagineum Seed Extract [CO_2]

Echium seed oil is unusual in that it contains a unique ratio of omega 6 and omega 3 essential fatty acids. It has the same gamma linolenic acid (GLA) content as evening primrose oil.

Echium oil also contains between 12 and 14% stearidonic acid compared to 2% found in the only other available commercial source, blackcurrant seed oil. Stearidonic acid reduces skin inflammation by suppressing the release of arachidonic acid, amongst other cell activities.

The significant levels of EFAs and GLA contained in echium oil should alone warrant interest, while the recent and ongoing research highlighting stearidonic acid's important role in reducing skin inflammation shows that echium oil is unparalleled in its effectiveness for skin care applications.

Excellent for adding to anti-wrinkle and after sun products.

Rosemary CO_2 Extract

See 'Rosemary Antioxidant (Botanical CO_2 Extracts)' in the antioxidants section on page 18.

Sea Buckthorn Pulp CO_2 Extract

INCI name: Hippophae rhamnoides Pulp Extract [CO_2]

Alleviates sunburn, promotes cell rejuvenation, has excellent pain- and stress- relieving and anti-inflammatory properties. Sea buckthorn berries contain nutrients and vitamins in their seeds, pulp and juice. These nutrients include vitamins A, K, E, C, B1, B2, folic acid, essential fatty acids, lipids, amino acids, and minerals. Sea buckthorn berries are second only to rosehips and acerola in vitamin C content. The high concentration (approximately 38%) of the palmitoleic fatty acid omega 7 in the pulp oil: is rarely found in the plant kingdom; is a natural component of human skin and plays an important role in the cellular regeneration of skin; and provides an elegant skin feeling. For more information about palmitoleic acid, see Macadamia Nut Oil on page 111. The extract is also rich in antioxidants, tocopherols, tocotrienols and phytosterols. It also gives products a beautiful reddish-orange colour that doesn't stain clothes.

Sea buckthorn pulp CO_2 extract has shown to have a wide range of beneficial health effects, namely:

- Anti-inflammatory and pain relieving effects

- Healing sunburn and wounds quickly by supporting the epithelisation and regeneration of skin tissue

- Using it in sun care products, as the oil seems to both enhance tanning and absorb UV rays - Russian cosmonauts even use it for protection against radiation burns in space!

- Healing acute and chronic phlegmonic acne when applied in 5% ointment bindings supplemented by a daily oral intake of the oil

- Balancing dry, mature, wrinkled skin to help restore elasticity and firmness.

- Regenerating and healing damaged, infected and sensitive skin

- Reducing oxidation (scavenging free radicals).

Substances not suitable for use in skin, hair and body care products

Non-suitable Vegetable Oils

Linseed/Flaxseed Oil

INCI name: Linum usitatissimum

Due to the high content of polyunsaturated fatty acids (omega 3) found in linseed (also called flaxseed) oil, it can go rancid after 2 weeks if not stored in nitrogen-flushed and capped bottles. Even if it is, I do not recommend that you use linseed oil in any skin care products, as it will turn your product rancid almost immediately. The same goes for wheatgerm oil, which will go rancid a few weeks after its production.

Taking Linseed Oil internally

Linseed oil is high in omega 3s but it is too volatile, and can go rancid after two weeks. It is possible to take it internally under the right conditions, such as if it is stored correctly. The only way to store linseed oil safely is to use the method which nutritionist Udo Erasmus uses to produce, bottle and store 'Udo's Choice Ultimate Oil Blend', i.e. to use cold pressed oil, which has been protected from heat, light and oxygen and then put into amber glass bottles which have been nitrogen flushed and stored in a refrigerator to ensure maximum stability.

Vegetable Oil alternatives to Linseed or Fish Oil

Fish oil capsules may appear to be only omega 3-rich alternative left as a nutritional supplement. However, you could instead make use of the omega 3-rich vegetarian alternatives of taking kiwi seed, rosehip or camelina vegetable oils. These oils can be taken internally by taking a teaspoon at a time or in salad dressings. For use in skin care products, they can be added to vegetable oil blends, creams and lotions. The skin absorbs these oils very rapidly and they will be in your bloodstream in a few minutes after applying them to the skin. Using fish oils on your face is not acceptable for me as a vegetarian, or probably the most sociable thing for anyone to do!

Wheatgerm Oil

INCI name: Triticum vulgare

By adding wheatgerm oil to your blend, cream or other product, you reduce the shelf life of the product.

Aromatherapists have written many books recommending the addition of up to 5% of wheatgerm oil to products to keep them from going rancid. In fact, it does the opposite. When starting my natural skin care factory in Sweden in the 1980s, I believed the British books, and I added 5% wheatgerm oil to my recipes. The shelf life of my products was 8-10 months, at which time they would smell rancid. This is because wheatgerm oil contains very little vitamin E oil (0.4-0.5%). It also contains a large amount of alpha linolenic acid that makes this rancidity process even faster. In addition, a rancid product accelerates the rancidity process of the skin and because of this we get wrinkles. Later, a friend and researcher into vitamin E oil convinced me to add 100% undiluted food grade vitamin E oil for its antioxidant properties to my products and the shelf life more than doubled, to about 2 years. For me that is proof enough. No large commercial cosmetics company adds wheatgerm oil to their products, as they know better. It seems to be used only in aromatherapy circles. I believe that many people believe that the smell of wheatgerm oil when rancid is the oil's usual smell but really it's often simply rancid. It smells quite different when it isn't rancid. Unfortunately the old aromatherapy books are still out there but I believe that the authors now know that they were wrong about wheatgerm oil and its antioxidant capabilities.

Comedogenic

Both linseed and wheatgerm oils are highly comedogenic. This means that they should never be used on acne or acne-prone skin. Comedogenic means that a topical substance tends to cause a build-up of dead cells, resulting in the development of comedones, which possibly leads to worsening acne eruptions. Comedones are also known as blackheads, which are small, flesh coloured, white, or dark bumps that give skin a rough texture. The bumps are found at the opening of a pore.

Mineral Oils and products

Mineral oils and products are definitely not suited for use in skin, hair or body care products.

Both paraffin and Vaseline® are produced from rock oil (literally 'petro' meaning 'rock' and 'oleum' meaning oil, hence the term: petroleum). Rock oil cannot practically be used in the form it is in when extracted. The raw oil must undergo extensive chemical and physical processing. The oil is distilled in refineries and different fractions are procured at different temperatures, e.g. propane, gasoline, petrol, photogen, asphalt, etc. Different substances are made from some of these fractions i.e. plastics, solvents, emulsifiers, medicines, flavourings and scents, textiles and many of the other products upon which our modern civilisation has been built.

Paraffin

INCI name: Paraffinum Liquidum

Paraffin is a mixture of carbon and hydrogen, which is obtained after distillation of raw rock oil. This is liquid or solid and has no taste or smell. It is soluble in fats and oils and does not go rancid.

Paraffin is used in ointments, creams, lotions, massage and skin oils, well-known baby oils and ointments and other oils as a constituent. It is even used as an ingredient in laxatives for chronic constipation. Used internally on a regular basis it can create certain side effects. It prevents absorption of the fat-soluble vitamins A, D, E, F and K and certain mineral compounds. Paraffin oil is also used as sewing machine oil, lubrication oil, for lighting, as floor wax, in chewing gum, etc.

Vaseline®

INCI name: Petrolatum

Vaseline® is a mixture of carbon and hydrogen procured from what is left over after the process of photogen distillation. Vaseline® is white or slightly green yellow with an ointment-like consistency and is tasteless, odourless and soluble in fats and oils. It melts at 35-50°C.

It is used in ointments, creams and lip balms. It is also used to grease machines, to coat machine parts to prevent rusting, to soften leather and as a lubricant.

The effects of Mineral Oils on the skin

The effects of applying paraffin oil and Vaseline® to the skin are that they strengthen the skin's protective qualities, but to such an extent that the skin completely closes off. They create a thin membrane on the surface of the skin, blocking the pores, which then more easily become enlarged and allow blackheads to form. They prevent the secretion of sweat and obstruct the skin's own production of fat. The skin cannot absorb pure paraffin or Vaseline®, except through emulsification, which tricks the skin into absorbing it. Because these substances are completely foreign to our bodies they can cause tumours in connective tissue.

These mineral oils are used primarily for their softening and protective effects. Producers can claim that these products are moisturising and protective. Well, they do offer moisturising effects by acting as an occlusive (see page 4 for more information) and stopping transepidermal water loss.

With regard to their protective qualities, it becomes more problematic as mineral oil-based products clog the pores by 40-60%. Now imagine that you permanently have half your body wrapped in clingfilm: that's how regularly using skin care products containing mineral oils affects your skin. You cannot, however, just wash the mineral-based product off your skin that easily because it fills your pores in the manner of plastic particles. You can compare the effect with trying to wash mineral-based paint from your hands with just soap and water; it doesn't work very well and it usually takes several washes to be rid of it. Mineral oil-based products can offer useful protection against water and certain chemicals, but when used over a long period of time, they often produce the opposite effects, namely that the skin becomes dry and lifeless and wholly dependent on the oils.

Mineral Oils	Vegetable Fats & Oils
Are not absorbed by the skin	Are easily absorbed by the skin
Are detrimental to the skin	Nurture the skin: are used as food by the skin
Do not contain Fatty Acids	Contain Fatty Acids that are vital for the body
Do not contain Essential Fatty Acids	Most of them contain Essential Fatty Acids
Do not contain any Vitamins	Contain vital Vitamins A, D and E, amongst others
Cosmetics containing only Mineral Oils can be kept for many years as they are dead products	Using Vegetable Oils in a product gives it an average shelf life of 2 to 2.5 years before the Vegetable Oils go rancid. Some Vegetable Fats and Oils last a lot longer.
Suppress the skin's own normal, healthy functioning	Stimulate the skin to function better and with long-term use, improve circulation

Table 3: The most important differences between Mineral Oils and Fats/Oils of vegetable origin

This is particularly noticeable with the use of petrochemical-based lip balms i.e. most of the well-known brands on the market! The irony is that most people have dry lips because of using these petrochemical-based lip balms. It's a cycle that never ends and people who use petrochemical-based lip balms to moisturise their lips have been misled in my view.

Some Useful Tips and Tables

Tips for buying Borage, Camelina, Evening Primrose, Hemp Seed, Kiwi Seed and Rosehip Oils

Due to their large percentage of omega 3 essential fatty acid or of GLA, these oils usually go rancid within 5-6 months. To extend their shelf lives to 2 years, 0.5% vitamin E oil or an equivalent antioxidant must be added soon after pressing. By the time you buy the oil, it's too late, so only buy it if it contains the added antioxidant, such as vitamin E, or it is sold in nitrogen-flushed bottles. There are many of these oils that are rancid for sale in the marketplace!

Tips for storing and using Vegetable Oils

If you look after your vegetable oils they will not only last longer but will also retain their inherent beneficial properties and therefore be more effective. Follow these simple guidelines to make the most of your vegetable oils.

- Vegetable oils should always be stored in sealed, airtight containers in a cool, dark room. It is very important to keep the lids on the bottles. Many people forget to put the lid straight back on the bottle after use and this exposure to oxygen can make oil go rancid very quickly. Similarly, exposure to sunlight makes oils go rancid and some oils are more light sensitive than others.

- When blending the oils for the recipes in this book, make sure that you stir the oils together with a spoon or spatula instead of shaking, so that you don't add extra oxygen.

- Due to the high percentage of vitamin E oil in some of the recipes, I have added another antioxidant, rosemary antioxidant (CO_2 extract) to prevent the vitamin E oil from oxidising. However, if you plan to use your product within 6 months of making it, you don't need to add the rosemary antioxidant.

Method for making and using Oil Compresses

1) Soak a clean muslin or cotton cloth in the oil and then squeeze out the oil so that it no longer drips from the cloth.

2) Wrap the cloth around the injured area.

3) Then wrap clingfilm around the cloth and cover with an elastic bandage to hold it all in place.

4) Leave on overnight.

Never use the same type of compress two nights in a row. Alternate with other compresses. For more information on compresses, see *The Aromantic Guide to the use of Herbs in Skin, Hair and Health Care products.*

Table 4: Fatty Acid content and other properties of some popular Vegetable Oils

Vegetable Oil \ Type of Fatty Acids:	Saturated	Mono unsaturated (Omega 7&9)	Duo unsaturated (Omega 6)	Poly unsaturated (Omega 3)	Absorption Note	Freezing Point	Fattiness Classification	Skin absorption time	Other classifications
Kiwi Seed	8%	12%	15%	65%	Top	-20°C	VVD	Very, very quick	Thin, soft, smooth, short
Linseed	17%	38%	13%	58%	Top	-25°C	VVD		Thin, rough, short
Camelina	14%	48%	25%	42%	Top	-15 to -18°C	VD		Thin, rough, short
Rosehip Seed	11%	21%	48%	36%	Top	under -15°C	D-vd		Soft, smooth, long
Hemp Seed	10%	13%	80%	25%	Top	under -20°C	VVD		Rough, short
Evening Primrose	10%	11%	85.5%	<1%	Top	-10°C	VD	Half slow	Half-soft, half-smooth, short
Borage	15%	31%	59%	≤0.4%	Top	-5°C	VD		Short, half-rough
Walnut	11%	20%	65%	14%	Top	0°C	HD		Soft, short
Thistle	11%	18.5%	81%	1%	Top	-10 to -20°C	D-vd		Rough, half-long
Grape Seed	18%	22%	80%	1%	Top	-5°C	D		Thin, soft, long
Sunflower	14%	36.5%	70%	0.5%	Mid.	-16 to -18°C	D		Little rough, half-long
Pumpkin Seed	22%	45%	50%	15%	Mid.	-15°C	Hf-hd	Slow	Half-soft, long
Mustard Seed	5%	51%	30%	15%	Mid.	unknown to me	Hf-hd		Warm, long
Sesame	18.5%	47%	45%	1.5%	Mid.	-3 to -6°C	Hf-hd		Soft, smooth, long
Argan	18%	44%	40%	0%	Mid.	+5°C	Hf-hd		Soft, smooth, long
Rice Bran	20%	44%	40%	2%	Mid.	-5 to -10°C	HF-hd		Soft, smooth, long

/contd

/contd

Vegetable Oil	Saturated	Mono unsaturated (Omega 7&9)	Duo unsaturated (Omega 6)	Poly unsaturated (Omega 3)	Absorption Note	Freezing Point	Fattiness Classification	Skin absorption time	Other classifications
Avocado	24%	80%	14%	1%	Mid.	+5°C	HF		Thin, soft, long
Hazelnut	10%	85%	19%	<1%	Mid.	under -20°C	HD		Soft, smooth, long
Jojoba	3%	97%	0.3%	0.2%	Mid.	+5°C	HF		Soft, very long
Apricot Kernel	9%	69%	34%	0.5%	Mid.	-15°C	F		Soft, smooth, long
Peach Kernel	11.5%	66%	30%	1%	Mid.	-15°C	F		Soft, smooth, long
Almond, Sweet	10%	80%	28%	0.5%	Mid.	-18°C	F		Soft, smooth, long
Shea Butter Oil	16%	71%	12%	1%	Base	+5 to +15°C	VF	Very, very slow	Soft, smooth, long
Olive	22%	86%	9%	<1.5%	Base	0 to +5°C	F-hf		Soft, long
Macadamia Nut	20.5%	89.5%	5%	2%	Base	+5°C	Vf-F		Soft, smooth, long
Moringa	27%	72%	1.1%	<0.5%	Base	+20°C	VF		Soft, long
Castor	3%	97%	6%	0%	Base	-15°C	VF		Thick, sticky, soft, short
Neem	40%	54%	16%	0%	Base	+15 to +20°C	VF		Thick, sticky, short
Coconut Oil	100%	0%	0%	0%	Base	-10°C	F		Soft, smooth, long

Please note: as the percentages in this chart are for the maximum amount of Fatty Acid content found in the Oil, they may add up to more than 100%. The Vegetable Oils are listed in according to their Absorption Note, Fattiness Classification and Skin Absorption Time.

Key: VVD=Very, very dry. VD=Very dry. D=Dry. D-vd=Dry to very dry. HF-hd=Half-fatty to half-dry. HF=Half-fatty. F=Fatty. VF=Very fatty. F-hf=Fatty to half-fatty. Vf-F=Very fatty to fatty (Lower case 'f' or 'v' denotes less fatty or dry oils than upper case 'F' or 'V'). Mid.=Middle

Table 5: Percentages of some popular Vegetable Oils to use in different products

Vegetable Oil	Order of suitability	Creams		Face Oils/ Serums		Body Oils	
	(SKIN TYPE)	DRY/ MAT/ SENS	OILY/ LARGE PORED	DRY/ MAT/ SENS	OILY/ LARGE PORED	DRY/ MAT/ SENS	OILY/ LARGE PORED
Kiwi Seed	OSMD	4-6	5-6	60-85	70-85	25-35	35-45
Camelina	ODMS	4-6	5-6	20-75	30-80	15-30	20-50
Rosehip Seed	OSDM	6-8	4-8	60-85	60-85	20-35	20-50
Hemp Seed	ODMS	8-10	5-6	40-50	50-60	15-20	20-30
Evening Primrose	ODMS	5-10	5-7	30-40	50-60	15-20	30-40
Borage	OMDS	5-10	5-7	30-40	50-60	15-20	30-40
Walnut	ODMS	6-8	4-5	20-40	20-50	25-30	30-35
Thistle	OMDS	2-12	2-6	30-50	30-50	15-20	20-30
Grape Seed	SODM	-	-	15-20	25-30	30-50	30-50
Sunflower	DOSM	10-12	4-5	30-40	25-30	30-50	25-30
Pumpkin Seed	DOMS	4-6	-	10-15	5-10	15-20	10-12
Sesame	DMSO	6-8	4-5	10-20	5-10	15-40	10-12
Argan	MSDO	6-8	4-5	10-20	5-10	25-30	10-15
Rice Bran	DSMO	8-10	2-4	20-50	10-15	30-60	10-20
Avocado	DMSO	10-12	2-4	15-30	8-10	40-50	10-15
Hazelnut	SMDO	5-6	5-6	10-30	10-15	30-40	10-20
Jojoba	ODMS	5-7	4-5	15-20	15-20	40-50	40-50
Apricot Kernel	SMDO	8-12	2-4	20-25	8-10	25-35	10-15
Peach Kernel	SMDO	8-12	2-4	20-25	8-10	25-35	10-15
Almond, Sweet	SMDO	6-8	2-4	20-25	8-10	25-35	10-15
Shea Butter Oil	DMS	7-9	-	10-30	-	10-30	-
Olive	DMS	5-7	-	5-10	-	10-30	-
Macadamia Nut	MDS	10-12	-	30-50	-	30-50	-
Moringa	MDS	8-10	-	20-30	-	20-40	-
Castor	DMS	5-6	-	-	-	5-10	-
Coconut, Liquid Fractionated	MDS	-	-	5-10	-	10-50	-

Key: D=Dry M=Mature S=Sensitive O=Oily. The second column, the order of suitability, refers to which skin types the oil is most suitable for, e.g. in Kiwi Seed, it is 'OSMD', so it is most suitable for oily skin and least suitable for dry skin.

Table 6: How to choose between Borage and Evening Primrose Oil

Properties	Borage Oil	Evening Primrose Oil
GLA content	16-24%	8-12%
Odour	Mouldy odour, which can be masked	Neutral smell when not rancid
Long/Short Oil	Short	Short
Softness on skin	Half-soft	Half-soft
Smooth/Rough	Half-rough	Half-smooth
Research	Not researched	Very well researched and documented
Dry/Oily	Very, very dry	Very Dry

Table 7: Metric-US conversion table: Volume (Liquid)

American Standard (cups & quarts)	American Standard (fluid ounces)	Metric (millilitres & litres)
⅛ teaspoon		0.5ml
¼ teaspoon		1ml
½ teaspoon		2ml
¾ teaspoon		4ml
1 teaspoon		5ml
½ tablespoon	¼ fl.oz	8ml
1 tablespoon	½ fl.oz	15ml
2 tablespoon	1 fl.oz	30ml
⅛ cup		35ml
¼ cup	2 fl.oz	65ml
⅓ cup		85ml
⅜ cup		95ml
½ cup	4 fl.oz	125ml
⅝ cup		160ml
⅔ cup		170ml
¾ cup		190ml
⅞ cup		220ml
1 cup	8 fl.oz	250ml
1½ cup	12 fl.oz	375ml
2 cups/1 pint	16 fl.oz	500ml
4 cups/1 quart	32 fl.oz	1 litre
1 gallon	128 fl.oz	4 litres

Table 8: Temperature

Celsius (°C)	Fahrenheit (F)
10	50
15	59
20	68
25	77
30	86
35	95
40	104
45	113
50	122
60	140
65	149
70	158
75	167
80	176
85	185
90	194
95	203
100	212

Apricot Kernel Oil

Apricot
INCI name: Prunus armeniaca

Description

This oil is extracted, either through cold or hot pressing without a solvent, from the kernel of apricot fruit, which consists of 40-50% oil. It is a stable, semi-fatty, light yellow oil, which keeps well and has its own taste and smell. It has a soft and smooth feel on the skin. Its qualities are that it spreads well and is easily absorbed by the skin. It is absorbed quite slowly (between 20-50 minutes) and is therefore excellent for use in whole body massage oil blends. It is a long oil (see page 12 for more information) and therefore offers excellent lubrication. It is a mild oil, which is tolerated by most people, especially those with sensitive, inflamed, dry or aging skin. It enhances skin elasticity.

The SAP value for apricot kernel oil is 135g.

Absorption Note
Middle.

Natural Vitamin Content
0.008%, or 8mg per 100ml of apricot kernel oil of vitamin E; 2-3% vitamin B17 (amygdalin).

Origin
Apricot trees are grown in California, parts of Asia and originate in Kashmir/ Mongolia.

Shelf Life
2-3 years.

Freezing Point
-15°C (+59°F).

About amygdalin

Apricot kernels are, like most nuts and seeds, very nutritious. Among the compounds they contain is one called amygdalin, which is sometimes called vitamin B17 or laetrile. Amygdalin is particularly prevalent in the seeds of those fruits in the *Prunus rosacea* family (bitter almond, apricot, blackthorn, cherry, nectarine, peach and plum). It is found in natural foods that contain nitriloside and has been used and studied extensively for well over 100 years. It is also contained in grasses, maize, sorghum, millet, cassava, linseed, apple seeds, and many other foods that, generally, have disappeared to a large extent from the western/industrialised nation's diet. Fruit kernels or seeds generally have other nutrients as well, some protein, unsaturated fatty acids, and various minerals. The most common source of vitamin B17 is the apricot kernel and is present in about a 2-3 percent level of concentration within the seed kernel. This substance is thought by some to attack cancer cells, and thus can help prevent cancer from breaking out in our bodies. Some clinical studies have been unsuccessful but others have shown amygdalin to be a successful anti-tumour agent. Peoples throughout the world who still eat a traditional diet rich in amygdalin have been found to be largely free from cancer. These diets are rich in foods containing amygdalin. Dr McCarrison studied the Hunza people of an area in northern Pakistan for several years in the 1920s and his account of these isolated people made their longevity and good health famous. He discovered no cancer in the Hunza people. Their diet contained over 200 times more vitamin B17 than industrialised nations. There was no such thing as money in their land. The number of apricot trees they owned measured a family's wealth. The thousands of seeds they did not eat, they stored or ground very finely and then pressed them to produce a very rich oil used in cooking and skin care. They used the apricot, its seed and the oil for practically everything. In addition to the apricot, these people mainly ate grain and fresh fruit and vegetables. These include buckwheat, millet, alfalfa, peas, broad beans, turnips, lettuce, apples, pears, peaches, mulberries, black and red cherries, and grapes, and sprouting pulses. Most of these contain vitamin B17, or amygdalin.

Uses of Apricot Kernel Oil

- It is the classic skin oil for sensitive skin.
- All the *Prunus* oils, i.e. almond, peach and apricot kernel oils have very similar properties and effects on the skin and all leave the skin feeling soft and smooth. Peach and apricot are the most similar.
- I regard peach and apricot kernel oils to be interchangeable for products that treat sensitive skin. They will always form the basis for any product I make for that skin type, with the exception of sensitive skin that is also oily. In that case rosehip or kiwi seed oils would form the basis of the recipe.
- In anti-wrinkle/skin rejuvenation products for sensitive skin.
- In massage lotions and oils for sensitive skin. Apricot kernel oil is a long oil and therefore offers good lubrication for massage.
- In skin cleansers and peelers for sensitive skin.
- In acne treatment creams and oil blends.
- In products that treat eczema and itchy skin conditions.
- In lip balms. Simply replace the vegetable oil/s in the recipe with apricot kernel oil.
- Used as cooking oil in Asia but seldom used for cooking in Europe.

Fatty Acid (Maximum) Content of Apricot Kernel Oil

Please note, the percentages below are for the maximum amount of fatty acid content found in apricot kernel oil, they may add up to more than 100%.

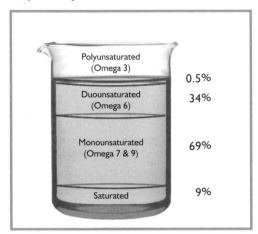

Polyunsaturated (Omega 3)	0.5%
Duounsaturated (Omega 6)	34%
Monounsaturated (Omega 7 & 9)	69%
Saturated	9%

Breakdown of Fatty Acid content of Apricot Kernel Oil	
Saturated	Palmitic Acid 3-7% Stearic Acid 0.5-1.5% Arachidic Acid <0.5%
Mono-unsaturated	Oleic Acid 56-68% Palmitoleic Acid 0.5-1%
Duo-unsaturated	Linoleic Acid 25-34%
Poly-unsaturated	Alpha Linolenic Acid 0.5%

Apricot Kernel Oil Sample Recipes

These Recipes make 100ml.

Face Oil for sensitive skin

20ml Apricot Kernel Oil
50ml Evening Primrose Oil
20ml Rosehip Oil
10ml/g Vitamin E Oil (undiluted)
5 drops Rosemary Antioxidant (CO_2 Extract)

Swedish Massage Oil for sensitive skin

50ml Apricot Kernel Oil
17ml Macadamia Nut Oil
15g Coconut Butter (melt in a bain-marie and add to the blend)
5ml Evening Primrose Oil
10ml Peach Kernel Oil
3ml/g Vitamin E Oil (undiluted)

Baby Oil for daily use

50ml Apricot Kernel Oil
25ml Rosehip Oil
20ml Calendula Oil
5ml/g Vitamin E Oil (undiluted)

Anti-Wrinkle Oil for sensitive skin

45ml Apricot Kernel Oil
18ml Rosehip Oil
10ml Evening Primrose Oil
5ml Peach Kernel Oil
20ml/g Vitamin E Oil (undiluted)
1ml/g Echium CO_2 Extract
1ml/g Sea Buckthorn CO_2 Extract
5 drops Rosemary Antioxidant (CO_2 Extract)

Acne Treatment Oil for everyday use

20ml Apricot Kernel Oil
20ml Borage Oil
20ml Rosehip Oil
11.5ml Thistle Oil
10ml Jojoba Oil
15ml/g Vitamin E Oil (undiluted)
2ml/g Vitamin A Palmitate
1.5ml Aromantic's Anti-Acne Active Formula
5 drops Rosemary Antioxidant (CO_2 Extract)

Percentages of Apricot Kernel Oil to use in products

Product	Product details	How much Oil you can use in the product	Average use
Creams	Sensitive skin	up to 15%	10-12%
	Mature, dry skin	up to 12%	8-10%
Massage and Body Care products	Whole Body Massage/Skin Oils for sensitive skin	up to 70%	
	Whole Body Massage/Skin Oils for all other skin types	up to 40%	
	Massage Lotions for sensitive skin	Up to 60% - remember to use Emulsifan CB Emulsifier.	40-50%
	Massage Lotions for all other skin types	up to 40%	20-30%
Acne Treatment products	Treatment Creams	up to 10%	5-6%
	Treatment Oils	up to 30%	15-20%
Eczema and Psoriasis Treatment products	Treatment Creams	up to 15%	6-8%
	Treatment Oils	up to 40%	20-30%
Skin Rejuvenation/ Anti-Wrinkle products for sensitive skin	Creams	up to 12%	10-12%
	Face Oils/Serums	up to 30%	20-25%
	Rejuvenating Body Oils	up to 50%	25-35%
	Eye Creams	up to 10%	6-8%
Cleansing and Peeling products for sensitive skin	Cleansing Oils	up to 70%	
	Cleansing or Peeling Creams	up to 50%	20-30%
Baby products	Everyday use Baby Oil	up to 70%	
	Everyday use Baby Creams	up to 16%	12-14%
Anti-itching products	Anti-itching Skin Oil	up to 60%	
Lip products	Lip Balms	Replace up to 100% of the Vegetable Oil content in the Recipe.	

Table 9: Percentages of Apricot Kernel oil to use in products

Argan Oil

© equinom. Image from BigStockPhoto.com

Argan

INCI name: Argania spinosa

Description

Argan oil comes from the nuts of the argan tree. It is a half-fatty oil with a high content of alpha tocopherols, carotene, phytosterols and omega 6 (duounsaturated) fatty acids. The fruit of the argan tree is green and looks like an olive but is larger and rounder. Inside, there is a hard-shelled nut, which represents about one quarter of the flesh fruit weight. The nut can contain up to three kernels from which the argan oil is extracted. The production of this oil is a demanding and laborious process, which was until recently done by hand. It takes about 100kg of fruits to make just 2-3 litres of oil. Recently, mechanical presses have been introduced to extract argan oil, which makes the process cheaper.

The SAP value for argan oil is unknown to me.

Absorption Note

Middle.

Natural Vitamin Content

Said to be rich in vitamins A, B1, B2, and B6 and has a high vitamin E content i.e. 0.02%), or 20mg per 100ml of argan oil.

Origin

This tree is unknown to many people since it grows only in the southwestern part of Morocco.

Shelf Life

Keeps for 2 years.

Freezing Point

Approximately +5 °C (+41 °F).

Uses of Argan Oil

- Argan oil is rich in omega 6 essential fatty acids, which stimulate, protect and regenerate the skin, helping to make it soft, supple and elastic.
- It aids skin healing and has a soothing effect on the body/skin.
- In before and after sun care products.
- Excellent ingredient for use in skin regeneration products for damaged or mature skin.

- It is said to be especially good for the regeneration of the skin in the upper chest and neck area.
- In eye care products treating sensitive and wrinkled areas around the eye.
- Acne and eczema treatment products.
- The oil has a nutty aroma and tastes very good in a salad dressing combined with lemon juice.

Fatty Acid (Maximum) Content of Argan Oil

Please note, as the percentages in this illustration are for the maximum amount of fatty acid content found in argan oil, they may add up to more than 100%.

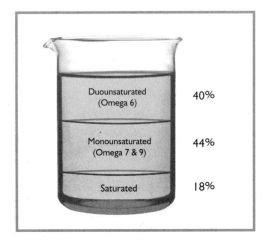

Duounsaturated (Omega 6)	40%
Monounsaturated (Omega 7 & 9)	44%
Saturated	18%

Breakdown of Fatty Acid content of Argan Oil	
Saturated	Palmitic Acid 12%
	Stearic Acid 6%
Mono-unsaturated	Oleic Acid 40-43%
	Palmitoleic Acid <0.5-1%
Duo-unsaturated	Linoleic Acid 37-40%

Argan Oil Sample Recipes

These Recipes make 100ml.

Argan Eye Oil

15ml Argan Oil
57.5ml Rosehip Oil
15ml Hemp Seed Oil
10ml/g Vitamin E Oil (undiluted)
1ml/g Calendula CO_2 Extract
1.5ml Aromantic's Anti-Acne Active Formula
5 drops Rosemary Antioxidant (CO_2 Extract)

Upper Neck and Chest Regeneration Oil

20ml Argan Oil
37ml Thistle Oil
30ml Evening Primrose Oil
5ml Pumpkin Seed Oil
8ml/g Vitamin E Oil (undiluted)
5 drops Rosemary Antioxidant (CO_2 Extract)

Daily Acne Treatment Oil

You can use this oil every day in the morning and evening.
8ml Argan Oil
67.5ml Rosehip Oil
10ml Jojoba Oil
10ml/g Vitamin E Oil (undiluted)
2ml/g Vitamin A Palmitate
1ml/g Calendula CO_2 Extract
1.5ml/g Anti-Acne Active Formula
5 drops Rosemary Antioxidant (CO_2 Extract)

Rejuvenating Face Oil/Serum

Suitable for all skin types.

10ml Argan Oil
25ml Borage Oil
40ml Rosehip Oil
25ml/g Vitamin E Oil (undiluted)
5 drops Rosemary Antioxidant (CO_2 Extract)

After Sun Oil

20ml Argan Oil
20ml Camelina Oil
20ml Evening Primrose Oil
20ml Rosehip Oil
10ml St. John's Wort Oil
10ml/g Vitamin E Oil (undiluted)
5 drops Rosemary Antioxidant (CO_2 Extract)

Percentages of Argan Oil to use in products

Product	Specific use of product	How much Oil you can use in the product	Average use
Upper Chest/ Neck area Regeneration products	Oil Blends	up to 20%	
	Creams	up to 10%	6-8%
Skin Rejuvenation/ Anti-Wrinkle products	Face Oils/Serums for dry, mature and sensitive skin types	up to 20%	
	Face Oils/Serums for oily skin	up to 10%	
	Rejuvenating Body Oils (all skin types)	up to 30%	
	Eye Care Oils	up to 30%	
	Eye Creams	up to 8%	4-6%
Sun Care products	Before and After Sun Oils	up to 20%	
	Sun Protection Creams	up to 15%	8-10%
	Sun Protection Lotions	up to 15%	5-6%
Eczema products	Creams	up to 20%	
	Treatment Oils	up to 8%	5-6%
Acne Treatment products	Treatment Oils	up to 12%	
	Treatment Creams	up to 6%	3-4%

Table 10: Percentages of Argan Oil to use in products

Avocado Oil

Avocado
INCI name: Persea gratissima

Description

Avocado oil is a mild, nourishing, semi-fatty oil, rich in vitamins. It is used when the skin is dry, tired and lacks lustre. The avocado tree is approximately 20 metres high and it bears a fruit, which is 5-20cm long. There are several varieties of avocados and these produce fruits, which differ from each other in size, taste and consistency. Traditionally, Mexicans and South Americans have used the mashed fruit pulp as protection against the sun and wind. The avocado pulp usually contains around 15-40% oil. The oil cannot be extracted from fresh fruits as the water and oil emulsify. The pulp is first dried until the fat content is between 40-80% of the weight. It is then cold pressed to extract the green oil and filtered.

The SAP value for avocado oil is 133-134g.

Absorption Note

Middle.

Important Natural Constituents

It contains a large quantity of non-lathering (unsaponifiable) substances (1.6-11%) including lecithin, betacarotene (the higher the quantity, the more yellow the oil is), vitamins E and D (more than in butter or eggs) and pantothenic acid (vitamin B5), but mostly different sterols which can have certain cosmetic effects. Also contains traces of chlorophyll, which makes the oil green.

Origin

Major producers today are Israel, South Africa, Brazil, Mexico, California, and the West Indies.

Shelf Life

Keeps for 2-5 years. To keep for longer than 2 years, store in dark, cool place under +10°C (+50°F).

Freezing Point

+5°C (+41°F) due to high content of saturated fatty acids.

Uses of Avocado Oil

- Good for dark skin, which produces less vitamin D in restricted sunlight, so especially useful to people with black skin living in the northern hemisphere, where there is not as much sunlight as in the southern hemisphere.

- Freshens, lifts and gives lustre to tired, dull and lacklustre skin. It works well for this purpose, especially when combined with rice bran oil.

- Keeps very well and is very stable.

- Especially good for dry and mature skin.

- In body oils.

- In anti-wrinkle and skin regeneration face oils and creams. These work especially well if left on overnight.

- Unrefined avocado oil helps to thicken the consistency of creams because of the high lecithin content in the oil, so therefore excellent for use in vegetal creams or in emulsions that separate easily.

- In menopause treatment body oil blends and creams. For menopausal products, always use with GLA-rich oils such as borage, evening primrose, hemp seed oil and arctic blackcurrant CO_2 extract or soya bean oil, which all help to balance the endocrine system.

- Avocado oil has a natural sun protection factor of 2-3, so excellent for adding to before and after sun care and sun protection products. When combined with vitamin E oil it is healing and soothing for sunburnt skin. Before sun oils: blend the avocado oil with sesame, rice bran, shea butter oil and vitamin E (undiluted) oils. To make after sun oils, blend the avocado oil with sea buckthorn CO_2 extract, and St. John's wort, rosehip, and vitamin E oils.

- Avocado is a long oil, which spreads well on the skin and is very quickly and thoroughly absorbed, despite its fattiness, so makes an excellent massage oil for whole body massage. For this purpose, always blend with drier oils, such as sunflower or grape seed oils.

- Avocado oil is unique in that it has a same feeling of fish oils on the skin and that of squalane, which is found in olive oil i.e. it is soft and long and thin. No other vegetable oil that I know of has that special feeling on the skin.

- Gives shine and softness to lip balms and adds glossiness to lipsticks. Simply replace the existing oils in your recipes with avocado oil.

- Excellent for adding, together with jojoba oil, to night creams and in protective ointments and creams e.g. hand creams. Because of its fattiness, it offers protection against the weather and wind and helps to keep moisture in the skin by stopping transepidermal water loss. In this way avocado oil works as an occlusive.

- When adding avocado oil to a cream or to an ointment (once it has cooled a little) you could add the oil during the third stage to protect its high vitamin content.

- In hair packs as it makes the hair shiny.

- Excellent oil for adding to anti-cellulite body and massage oil blends and creams.

- Add to body and massage oil blends that help to treat rheumatism. For this purpose, avocado oil combines well with, for example, St. John's wort, mullein, and comfrey oils and chamomile CO_2 extract and rosemary essential oil.

- In scrubbing/exfoliating products, e.g. combine the oil with fine sea salt to make the product.
- Although not used for cooking in countries of origin, it could be used because it can stand high temperatures (although this will destroy the vitamins).
- Taken internally, along with soya oil, for alleviating symptoms of female menopause.

Fatty Acid (Maximum) Content of Avocado Oil

Please note, as the percentages below are for the maximum amount of fatty acid content found in avocado oil, they may add up to more than 100%.

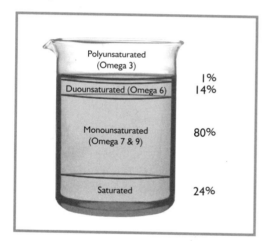

Breakdown of Fatty Acid content of Avocado Oil	
Saturated	Palmitic Acid 7-22%
	Stearic Acid 1-2%
Mono-unsaturated	Oleic Acid 59-70%
	Palmitoleic Acid 9-10%
Duo-unsaturated	Linoleic Acid 8-14%
Poly-unsaturated	Alpha Linolenic Acid ≤1%

Avocado Oil Sample Recipes

These Recipes make 100ml.

Regeneration Body Oil for black skin

50ml Avocado Oil
10ml Rosehip Oil
10ml Evening Primrose Oil
10g Coconut Butter (melt in a bain-marie before adding to the blend)
20ml/g Vitamin E Oil (undiluted)
5 drops Rosemary Antioxidant (CO_2 Extract)

Menopause Treatment Body Oil

30ml Avocado Oil
30ml Soya Bean Oil (**NB** must be cold pressed)
20ml Borage Oil
15ml Hemp Seed Oil
5ml/g Vitamin E Oil (undiluted)
5 drops Rosemary Antioxidant (CO_2 Extract)

After Sun Oil

44ml Avocado Oil
20ml Thistle Oil
10ml Rosehip Oil
5ml Evening Primrose Oil
4ml St. John's Wort Oil
15ml/g Vitamin E Oil (undiluted)
2ml/g Sea Buckthorn CO_2 Extract
5 drops Rosemary Antioxidant (CO_2 Extract)

Baby Oil for black skin

60ml Avocado Oil
30ml Thistle Oil
5ml Evening Primrose Oil
5ml/g Vitamin E Oil (undiluted)
5 drops Rosemary Antioxidant (CO_2 Extract)

Rheumatism Treatment Oil
68ml Avocado Oil
10ml St. John's Wort Oil
10ml Comfrey Oil
10ml/g Vitamin E Oil (undiluted)
2ml/g Chamomile CO_2 Extract
5 drops Rosemary Antioxidant (CO_2 Extract)

Massage Oil for black skin
50ml Avocado Oil
20ml Jojoba Oil
10ml Castor Oil
10ml Shea Butter Oil
8ml Thistle Oil
2ml/g Vitamin E Oil (undiluted)

Percentages of Avocado Oil to use in products

Product	Product details	How much Oil you can use in the product	Average use
Black or dark skin products	Creams	up to 20%	12-15%
	Skin and Body Oils	up to 60%	40-50%
	Whole Body Massage Oils	up to 70%	50-60%
Anti-Cellulite products	Creams	up to 16%	10-15%
	Body and Massage Oils	up to 40%	
Skin Rejuvenation/ Anti-Wrinkle products including black or dark skin	Face Oils/Serums for dry, mature and sensitive skin	Up to 30% - blend with drier Oils.	
	Face Oils for oily/large-pored skin	Up to 10% - blend with drier Oils.	
	Rejuvenating Body Oils for all skin types except oily/large-pored skin	up to 70%	
	Night Creams for intense Skin Rejuvenation	up to 15%	12-15%
Creams	Face Creams for dry/mature skin	up to 15%	10-12%
Menopause Treatment products	Body Oils	Up to 40% - remember to blend with GLA-rich Oils and CO_2 Extracts.	
	Treatment Creams	up to 15%	12-15%

/contd

/contd

Sun Care products	Sun Creams	up to 15%	12-15%
	Sun Oil (Before Sun)	Up to 50% - blend with recommended Oils.	
	Sun Oil (After Sun)	Up to 50% - blend with recommended Oils and Active Ingredients.	
Skin protection products *Always blend Avocado Oil with Jojoba Oil for protective products*	Protective Creams	up to 12%	6-8%
	Protective Ointments	up to 40%	20-30%
Lip products	Lip Balms & Lip Sticks	Follow Recipes and replace Oil in Recipe with Avocado Oil.	
Rheumatism Oil Blends		Up to 60% - remember to blend with recommended Oils and Active Ingredients.	
Massage Oils	For whole body massage	Up to 50% - remember to blend with recommended Oils and Active Ingredients.	
Skin Oils	For oily/large-pored skin	a maximum of 10%	
	For dry, mature, sensitive skin types	up to 70%	
	Baby Oils	up to 50%	
Scrubbing/Exfoliating products		Up to 35% - add up to 15% Castor Oil.	
Hair Care products	Hair Oil Packs to make hair shiny	up to 50%	

Table 11: Percentages of Avocado Oil to use in products

Borage Oil

Borage
INCI name: Borago officinalis

Description

Synonym: Starflower. The oil is pressed out of starflower seeds. The oil has a particular (mould-like) smell and colour. It contains a very different ratio of fatty acids, amongst these a very high percentage (20-24%) gamma linolenic acid (GLA), which is a very rare fatty acid also found in evening primrose oil (8-12%), and blackcurrant seed oil (approximately 6%). Gamma linolenic acid (GLA) is a duounsaturated fatty acid closely related to the duounsaturated essential fatty acid, linoleic acid. Both are substances the body needs to create prostaglandins. Borage oil is popularly used for skin rejuvenation and scar treatment products.

The SAP value for borage oil is 136g.

Absorption Note

Top.

Natural Vitamin Content

Traces of vitamins can be found in the original oil.

Origin

Indigenous to southern Europe but is now cultivated in North America and other places.

Shelf Life

Due to the high content of gamma linolenic acid you should never buy borage oil that does not have added vitamin E oil or other natural antioxidants, otherwise it will go rancid within 6 months. Adding 0.5% undiluted vitamin E oil, or an equivalent antioxidant, will increase the shelf life to 2 years.

Freezing Point

-5°C (+23°F).

Contraindications

If on medication, don't take borage oil internally as it can interfere with, or affect, other medication that you may be taking, especially non-steroidal anti-inflammatory drugs (NSAIDs) such as ibuprofen.

Further information

- See page 9 for more information about prostaglandins.
- See page 9 for 'Gamma linolenic acid and its function in the body'.
- See Table 6 on page 33 for 'How to choose between borage oil and evening primrose oil'
- See page 29 for 'Tips for buying borage, camelina, evening primrose, hemp seed, kiwi seed and rosehip oils'.

Fatty Acid (Maximum) Content of Borage Oil

Please note, as the percentages below are for the maximum amount of fatty acid content found in borage oil, they may add up to more than 100%.

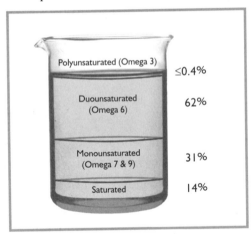

Breakdown of Fatty Acid content of Borage Oil	
Saturated	Palmitic Acid 9-11%
	Stearic Acid 3-4%
Mono-unsaturated	Oleic Acid 15-20%
	Palmitoleic Acid ≤0.5%
	Eicosenoic Acid 4-5%
	Erucic Acid 2-3%
	Nervonic Acid 0.5-2.5%
Duo-unsaturated	Linoleic Acid 34-38%
	Gamma Linolenic Acid (GLA) 16-24% (ave. of 21%)
Poly-unsaturated	Alpha Linolenic Acid ≤0.4%

Uses of Borage Oil

- Borage oil penetrates down and into the skin, which as a result becomes softer and is less prone to eczema and acne. It has a moisture-retaining effect, prevents drying of the skin, and increases the cells' ability to absorb oxygen and withstand disease. Borage and other oils containing gamma linolenic acid (GLA) are not miracle cures but can help to support the body's own functioning to maintain good health. Borage oil is often used in preference to evening primrose oil as it is said to have a much higher average GLA level (up to 24%).
- Borage oil is a short oil, which is absorbed by the skin quickly and does not leave an oily feeling on the skin. These properties make it an excellent choice for a face or skin oil but would not work well on its own as a massage oil that is used for long strokes (as in whole body massage). For this purpose, blend it with longer oils, such as jojoba oil.
- Works well for all skin care products that shouldn't be too oily.
- Good for all skin types, but works particularly well for mature and dry skin.
- Anti-wrinkle face oils and serums.
- Eye contour products.
- If adding borage oil to creams and lotions, always blend with fattier oils. The only exception to this would be if you were making creams and

lotions for oily skin, then you would blend it with dry oils.

- Oil treatment blends for healing scar tissue and wounds. Always add 50% vitamin E oil to your scar treatment oils. Adding comfrey oil will help to shrink keloids in scar tissue and will treat and strengthen veins after surgery. A keloid is a special type of scar that results in an overgrowth of tissue at the site of a healed skin injury. Keloids are not the same as hypertrophic scars, which are raised scars that do not grow beyond the boundaries of the original wound and may reduce over time. Both scars result from the body over-producing collagen at the site of an injury.

- In products that treat skin infections such as eczema, psoriasis and acne.

- In hair packs for treating dandruff.

- In wound-healing products.

- Always mix it with other vegetable oils for skin application, as it is too dry to use on its own.

- Due to the fact that borage oil is not as soft on the skin as evening primrose oil, I recommend using evening primrose oil for sensitive skin types. If you want to use borage oil in products for sensitive skin, then you could compensate by adding softer oils such as rosehip, kiwi seed, apricot kernel and peach kernel oils.

Tips for using Borage Oil

- My practical work over the last 20 years has shown me that it is necessary to add at least 5% borage oil to an oil blend or cream, otherwise it is not effective at all.

- Due to the naturally 'mouldy' smell of borage oil, it is a good idea to mix it with base note essential oils such as benzoin, patchouli, sandalwood or cedarwood.

Borage Oil Sample Recipes

These Recipes make 100ml.

Borage Anti-Wrinkle Face Oil for dry and mature skin

40ml Borage Oil
10ml Thistle Oil
20ml Rosehip Oil
9ml Peach Kernel Oil
20ml/g Vitamin E Oil (undiluted)
1ml/g Vitamin A Palmitate
5 drops Rosemary Antioxidant (CO_2 Extract)

Eczema Treatment Oil (dry type)

Apply 1-2 times a day.

30ml Borage Oil
40ml Thistle Oil
8ml Jojoba Oil
20ml/g Vitamin E Oil (undiluted)
2ml/g Vitamin A Palmitate
5 drops Rosemary Antioxidant (CO_2 Extract)

Scar Tissue Treatment Oil

This blend can help reduce keloid scars. Do not apply on open scars. If open, then apply around the area of the scar.

20ml Borage Oil
15ml Thistle Oil
13ml Rosehip Oil
50ml/g Vitamin E Oil (undiluted)
2ml/g Vitamin A Palmitate
1ml/g Calendula CO_2 Extract
10 drops Rosemary Antioxidant (CO_2 Extract)

Percentages of Borage Oil to use in products

Product	Product details	How much Oil you can use in the product	Average use
Skin and Face Oils	Oily/large-pored skin	up to 60%	
	Dry/mature skin	up to 40%	
	Sensitive skin	25%	
Skin Rejuvenation/ Anti-Wrinkle products	Anti-wrinkle Face Oils/Serums for all skin types	up to 60%	
GLA Creams	For dry, mature and sensitive skin types	up to 10%	5-10%
	For oily/large-pored skin	up to 8%	5-7%
Eye Contour products	Creams	up to 10%	5-8%
	Oil Blends	up to 40%	
Baby products	Creams	up to 10%	5-7%
	Everyday Baby Oils	up to 30%	20-25%
	Treatment Oils	up to 40%	25-30%
Eczema & Psoriasis products	Treatment Creams	up to 20%	5-10%
	Treatment Oils	up to 30%	25-30%
Acne Treatment products	Treatment Creams	up to 15%	8-10%
	Treatment Oils	up to 35%	20-25%
Dandruff Treatment products	Anti-Dandruff Oil Packs	up to 40%	
Massage products	Whole Body Massage Oils for dry, mature and sensitive skin types	up to 20%	5-10%
	Whole Body Massage Oils for oily/large-pored skin	up to 30%	10-15%
Scar tissue/post-surgery Treatment Oils		up to 35%	20-25%
Oil Blends that help wound healing		Up to 40% - together with Vitamin E Oil (undiluted) and Comfrey Oil.	

Table 12: Percentages of Borage Oil to use in products

Calendula Oil

© Serith. Image from BigStockPhoto.com

Calendula

INCI name: Calendula officinalis and usually the INCI name for the oil that the calendula is macerated in.

Description

Calendula (marigold) is one of the best known and versatile healing herbs and is rich in herbal history, widely used by herbalists throughout the centuries. Calendula is believed to have originated in or near the Mediterranean and is now naturalised all over the world. The herb is also known as common marigold or 'pot marigold' because the dried flowers were traditionally used in soups and stews to help ward off illness. Ancient Egyptians and Romans valued calendula highly, and, noticing that in their warm, temperate climates it was always in bloom on the first day of each month, called it 'calends', after the calendar. It is known as the 'flower of the sun', with its petals of golden orange. It has also been associated with the sun's journey across the sky because it opens when the sun rises and closes as it sets. The herbalists Culpeper and Gerard refer to calendula as a comforter of the heart and spirits.

An easy way to make macerated calendula oil is by using calendula CO_2 extract instead of using fresh botanical material to macerate in the base oil. Using the calendula CO_2 extract makes it much more potent; 1kg of the CO_2 extract is equivalent to 17-20kg of calendula flowers! Furthermore, the supercritical CO_2 extraction method extracts more of the constituents of the flowers than traditional oil maceration could ever do.

CO_2 extracts are becoming more and more popular as they offer a much more pure and concentrated form of the product than other types of extraction. They are also free of any solvent residues and diluting agents and are composed almost exclusively of the raw material's ingredients and can be used in a fairly low dosage. This low dosage means that a high quality, active cosmetic product can be created at a reduced cost. Due to the carotene content, the oil is a distinctive yellow-orange.

For the SAP value, refer to the oil that the calendula has been macerated in.

Natural Vitamin Content

Calendula contains high quantities of carotene. Refer to the vegetable oil that the calendula is macerated in for further vitamin content.

Origin

Calendula is native to southern Europe and Egypt.

Shelf Life

Refer to the oil that the calendula has been macerated in.

Freezing Point

Refer to the oil that the calendula has been macerated in.

Further information

- See page 29 for how to make an oil compress.

Fatty Acid (Maximum) Content of Calendula Oil

Refer to the fatty acid illustration and breakdown table of the oil that the calendula has been macerated in.

Uses of Calendula Oil

- Calendula provides effective treatment for most minor skin problems.
- Calendula, through the combined action of its essential oil, which is antibiotic, and other constituents, stimulate the immune system and enhance the body's fight against infection. It rapidly promotes skin tissue repair and minimises scar formation, is anti-inflammatory, and promotes granulation.
- Used for its healing and tissue-regenerating properties for all skin types and conditions, including sensitive skin and for babies.

- Calendula is good to use in all cases where cell regeneration is required such as in cases of sunburn, sores, where skin has been removed and also where the skin is red, itchy and irritated. It also increases skin pigmentation after sunbathing.
- In products that treat chronic, slow healing sores such as bedsores.
- Excellent for treating varicose ulcers and varicose veins.
- Also used for treating frostbite, burns and eczema.
- Other key actions of this plant are the following: astringent, heals wounds, antiseptic, antifungal, antibacterial, antiviral, and it contracts the capillaries (an action that explains its effectiveness for healing cuts, wounds, varicose veins, and various inflammatory conditions). For these effects, always blend calendula oil with comfrey oil as they have synergistic effects.
- It is used for cuts, scrapes, wounds, red and inflamed skin, including minor burns and sunburn, for acne, rashes, and fungal conditions. It is helpful for nappy rash and soothes nipples that are sore from breastfeeding. Always combine with St. John's wort oil for these conditions and for any kind of itchiness, add an infusion of chickweed to creams.
- In treatment oils that treat red and inflamed skin, blend the calendula oil with St. John's wort oil, vitamin E oil and vitamin A palmitate.
- Due to its carotene content, calendula ointment is excellent for healing chapped skin on hands and feet. The carotene is a powerful antioxidant and so works well to fight free radicals, the cause of the

chapped skin. ~~Also good for treating athlete's foot.~~

- For excellent healing ointments, add calendula oil, calendula tincture and calendula CO_2 extract to your ointment recipe. A simple calendula ointment compress can be made by applying a generous amount of ointment onto the affected hand or foot, cover it with a cotton gloves or cotton socks, then a plastic glove or bag, and finally with another cotton glove or cotton sock. Leave on overnight, repeat a few nights in a row and you will see an improvement in the healing of chapped skin in less than a week.

- In acne treatment oils, because of the properties of jojoba oil and the soothing effects of calendula. This is a very good blended oil for all types of acne products.

- In scar tissue treatment products. Can be used in early treatment of scars instead of comfrey oil (comfrey oil cannot be used until 2-3 months after the scarring has taken place). Calendula oil can then be used in combination with comfrey oil after the 2-3 month period has passed.

- In psoriasis and eczema treatment products.

- In hair care and treatment products for dry, irritated scalps, dandruff or scalp eczema. Add to shampoos as a fat restoring agent to replace omega fat restoring agent. It makes the shampoo creamy.

- In massage oils for whole body massage, for easing menstruation pain, PMS and digestive trouble. As it is a long oil, I recommend using a jojoba oil base for macerating the calendula CO_2 extract as it is very good for long massage strokes used in whole body massage.

Calendula Oil Sample Recipes

These Recipes make 100ml.

Calendula Skin Treatment Oil

For treating bedsores, wounds, varicose veins.

40ml Calendula Oil

20ml Comfrey Oil

13ml Thistle Oil

10ml Rosehip Oil

15ml/g Vitamin E Oil (undiluted)

2ml/g Sea Buckthorn CO_2 Extract

5 drops Rosemary Antioxidant (CO_2 Extract)

Calendula (or Marigold) Ointment

Stage 1

15g Beeswax

50ml Calendula Oil

Stage 2

22ml Thistle Oil

10ml Comfrey Oil

Stage 3

1ml (25 drops) Essential Oil

2ml/g Vitamin E Oil (undiluted)

Method

1) Melt Stage 1 in a bain-marie.

2) When melted, add Stage 2.

3) Cool down in a cool water basin and add Stage 3 when it has the consistency of a thick soup.

4) Put in a jar and seal well. It keeps for 2 years if stored in an airtight container in a cool, dark and dry place.

Tip

If you want to make a comfrey ointment, simply replace the calendula oil with comfrey oil.

Nappy Rash Treatment Oil

40ml Calendula Oil
30ml Rosehip Oil
8ml Comfrey Oil
10ml St. John's Wort Oil
10ml/g Vitamin E Oil (undiluted)
2ml/g Chamomile CO_2 Extract
5 drops Rosemary Antioxidant (CO_2 Extract)

Acne Treatment Oil

Apply every evening.
30ml Calendula Oil
30ml Borage Oil
27ml Thistle Oil
10ml/g Vitamin E Oil (undiluted)
1.5ml/g Aromantic's Anti-Acne Active Formula
1.5ml/g Vitamin A Palmitate
5 drops Rosemary Antioxidant (CO_2 Extract)

Scar Tissue Treatment Oil

Use in the first 2-3 months of the scar being formed.
25ml Calendula Oil
20ml Rosehip Oil
5ml Borage Oil
50ml/g Vitamin E Oil (undiluted)
10 drops Rosemary Antioxidant (CO_2 Extract)

Anti-Wrinkle/Skin Rejuvenation Oil

30ml Calendula Oil
50ml Rosehip Oil
18ml/g Vitamin E Oil (undiluted)
2ml/g Echium CO_2 Extract
5 drops Rosemary Antioxidant (CO_2 Extract)

Hair Treatment Oil

60ml Calendula Oil
20ml Thistle Oil
10g Coconut Butter (melt in a bain-marie and add it to the blend)
10ml/g Vitamin E Oil (undiluted)
5 drops Rosemary Antioxidant (CO_2 Extract)

After Sun Oil

40ml Calendula Oil
30ml Rosehip Oil
9ml St. John's Wort Oil
20ml/g Vitamin E Oil (undiluted)
1ml/g Vitamin A Palmitate
5 drops Rosemary Antioxidant (CO_2 Extract)

Percentages of Calendula Oil to use in products

Product	Product details	How much Oil you can use in the product	Average use
Treatment Oils	for e.g. bed sores, varicose veins and ulcers, wounds, etc	Up to 70% - remember to add comfrey oil to the blend.	
Sun Care products	Sun Oil (Before Sun)	up to 40%	
	Sun Oil (After Sun)/ Sun Burn Treatment Oil	up to 60%	
	Sun Creams	up to 15%	10-12%
Foot products	Foot Creams	up to 20%	10-12%
	Foot Ointments/ Compresses	up to 70%	
Acne Treatment products	Treatment Creams	up to 15%	6-8%
	Daily use Acne Treatment Oils	up to 25%	
Eczema and Psoriasis products	Treatment Creams	up to 15%	3-5%
	Treatment Oils	up to 35%	
Skin Soothing products for soothing or calming burns, itchy skin, rashes, nappy rash, nipples, etc	Soothing Creams	Up to 20% - remember to always blend with St. John's Wort Oil, which is soothing.	12-15%
	Soothing Treatment Oils	Up to 60% - blend with St. John's Wort Oil.	
Treatment Oils	Red and Inflamed Skin Treatment Oils	Up to 60% - remember to blend with St. John's Wort Oil, Vitamin E Oil and Vitamin A Palmitate.	
	Scar Tissue Treatment Oils	up to 50%	
Anti-Wrinkle/ Skin Rejuvenation products	Face Creams	up to 15%	12-15%
	Face and Body Oils	up to 40%	
Hair Care products	Dry Hair/Scalp Treatment Oils	up to 80%	
	In Dry Hair Shampoos as a Fat Restoring Agent	5-6%	
Massage Oil		up to 65%	

Table 13: Percentages of Calendula Oil to use in products

Camelina Oil

© Mary Ellen (Mel) Harte, Bugwood.org

Camelina
INCI name: Camelina sativa

Description

Synonyms: Gold of pleasure, wild flax, false flax, linseed dodder, German sesame, siberian oilseed.

Camelina is an annual or winter annual that attains the height of 30 to 90cm tall with branched or hairy stems that become woody at maturity. Leaves are arrow shaped, sharp pointed, 5-8cm long with sharp edges. Seed pods are 6-14mm long and superficially resemble the mature fruit of the flax plant, which is a dry 'boll'. Crushing and pressing the seed produces the oil and the seeds yields between 37-43% oil. Camelina oil is golden coloured with a distinctive rich green aroma. The non-organic oil has a more neutral smell than the organic. Camelina oil contains exceptionally high levels (up to 42%) of omega 3 fatty acids, which is uncommon in vegetable sources. The major components are approximately 15-20% linoleic acid (omega 6); and 35-42% alpha linolenic acid (omega 3). It is also highly monounsaturated, naturally supplying more than 30% of stable, monounsaturated (oleic and gadoloeic) fatty acids. As a result, it does not promote the formation of harmful free radicals. Camelina has excellent emollient, cardiotonic, hypotensive, anticoagulant, anti-inflammatory, hydrating, and moisturising properties.

The SAP value for camelina oil is 126-132g.

Absorption Note

Top.

Natural Vitamin Content

The oil is also rich in antioxidants, such as tocopherols (type of vitamin E), making this a highly stable oil very resistant to oxidation and rancidity. The vitamin E content of camelina oil is approximately 10mg per 100g makes it the highest of all natural tocopherol sources. By contrast, flaxseed oil contains only traces of vitamin E.

Origin

It is native to northern Europe and to central Asian areas, but has been introduced to North America.

Shelf Life

Even though camelina oil has a very high natural vitamin E content, I still recommend that you buy camelina oil with 0.5% added vitamin E oil (or other similar strength natural antioxidant) because of the high content of polyunsaturated fatty acids. Adding 0.5% undiluted vitamin E oil, or an equivalent antioxidant, will increase the shelf life to 2 years.

Freezing Point

-15°C to -18°C (+5 to +0.4°F).

Contraindications/warnings

Best not used during pregnancy or on sensitive skin due to the 1-3% erucic acid content, which can make it a potential dermal irritant.

Further information

- See page 7 for 'More information about essential fatty acids (vitamin F).
- See page 15 for 'Rebalancing certain skin types with certain vegetable oils'.
- See page 29 for 'Tips for buying borage, camelina, evening primrose, hemp seed, kiwi seed and rosehip oils'.

Fatty Acid (Maximum) Content of Camelina Oil

Please note, as the percentages in this Illustration are for the maximum amount of fatty acid content found in camelina oil, they may add up to more than 100%.

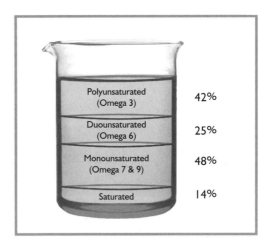

Polyunsaturated (Omega 3)	42%
Duounsaturated (Omega 6)	25%
Monounsaturated (Omega 7 & 9)	48%
Saturated	14%

Breakdown of Fatty Acid content of Camelina Oil	
Saturated	Palmitic Acid 3-8%
	Stearic Acid 2-3%
	Arachidic Acid 2%
	Lignoceric Acid 0.5%
	Lauric Acid 0.5%
	Behenic Acid 0.5%
Mono-unsaturated	Oleic Acid 12-27%
	Gadoleic Acid 9-17%
	Erucic Acid 1-3%
	Palmitoleic Acid 0.5%
Duo-unsaturated	Linoleic Acid 16-25%
Poly-unsaturated	Alpha Linolenic Acid 30-42%

Uses of Camelina Oil

- Excellent in anti-wrinkle/skin rejuvenation products.
- Because it is very high in omega 3 fatty acids (up to 42%), you can take it internally instead of marine oils or flaxseed oil in salad dressings or as a food supplement (1-2 teaspoons a day). However, due to its high content

of naturally occurring and added vitamin E, camelina oil will keep for 2 years and won't go rancid after 2 weeks such as flaxseed oil does. The exception to this is Udo Erasmus flax oil products, which are stored in bottles with lids and bottles that are nitrogen-flushed and customers are advised to store the oil in the fridge. Be aware that the organic camelina oil has a very strong, dominant taste so you may want to mix it with more neutral tasting oils.

- It's an excellent emollient with extremely good skin penetration. This, and its non-oiliness makes it a good choice for adding to body and face lotions.
- The very high percentage of linoleic acid improves the skin's elasticity and gives the skin a glossy luminescence in the same way as moringa oil does.
- Hydrating and moisturising.
- It's a very dry, thin, short oil, which feels rather rough on the skin. Due to this, it is important to always blend it with softer oils. In an anti-wrinkle oil blend, vitamin E oil is an excellent smooth and soft oil to blend camelina oil with as it also has the antioxidant properties needed for skin rejuvenation.
- Anti-inflammatory, so good for adding to products treating arthritis and rheumatism.
- Provides a protective coating for hair follicles, so can be used in protective hair and skin oils.
- Spreads well on the skin, so good for adding to massage oil blends.
- Especially beneficial in products treating mature and/or dry skin.
- Particularly effective in the treatment of skin conditions such as acne, eczema and psoriasis.

- Excellent for treating large-pored skin due to camelina oil's high content of omega 6 and 3 essential fatty acids, which help to reduce the size of pores.
- Camelina oil has a fatty acid content similar to that found in marine fauna such as sharks and the sperm whale and is now used as a replacement for sperm whale oil in cosmetics. It contains up to 17% gadoleic acid, which is also found in cod liver oil in significant quantities.
- When using camelina oil in your skin care products, be aware that the organic oil has a distinctive, richly green aroma while the non-organic oil has a more neutral smell. They both smell pleasantly of a fresh summer field.
- Because of its omega 3 content, camelina has similar properties to rosehip oil. However, rosehip oil should be used for sensitive skin and camelina oil can be used for all other skin types other than sensitive skin.

Camelina Oil and the future

Due to the high content of essential fatty acids, linoleic and alpha linolenic acids, which are known to reduce the low density lipoproteins (LDL or "bad cholesterol") level in the blood, so makes camelina a good oil for heart and cardiovascular health. For this reason, camelina oil may be a replacement for the internal use of marine oils due to its similar fatty acids. The oil contains many natural antioxidants, such as tocopherols, which make the oil stable and well suited for use as cooking oil. The vitamin E content of camelina oil is approximately 10mg per 100g. Camelina is now being marketed by companies as a functional food in a range of products from pure oil, salad dressing, to seeds and crushed oilseed cake. Because of the health effects, technical stability and almond-like taste camelina oil may be important food oil for the future.

Furthermore, research suggests its beneficial use in skin care products such as body lotions, bath foams, creams, soaps as well as soft detergents. Trials have also been undertaken in Austria to test the effectiveness of camelina as a raw material for liquid biofuel and although they were successful in the production of the fuel, the oil is not yet economically viable for this purpose.

Camelina Oil Sample Recipes

These Recipes make 100ml.

Everyday Camelina Acne Treatment Oil

60ml Camelina Oil
10ml Evening Primrose Oil
10ml Jojoba Oil
6.5ml Rosehip Oil
10ml/g Vitamin E Oil (undiluted)
2ml/g Vitamin A Palmitate
1.5ml Aromantic's Anti-Acne Active Formula
5 drops Rosemary Antioxidant (CO_2 Extract)

Camelina Rheumatism/Arthritis Treatment Oil

Use daily.
50ml Camelina Oil
30ml Borage Oil
10ml Rosehip Oil
10ml/g Vitamin E Oil (undiluted)
5 drops Rosemary Antioxidant (CO_2 Extract)

Glossy Anti-Wrinkle Cure Oil for oily skin

60ml Camelina Oil
20ml Evening Primrose Oil
8ml Jojoba Oil
10ml/g Vitamin E Oil (undiluted)
2ml/g Vitamin A Palmitate
5 drops Rosemary Antioxidant (CO_2 Extract)

Glossy Anti-Wrinkle Cure Oil for dry skin

75ml Camelina Oil
10ml Rosehip Oil
13ml/g Vitamin E Oil (undiluted)
2ml/g Vitamin A Palmitate
5 drops Rosemary Antioxidant (CO_2 Extract)

Glossy Face Cure/Anti-Wrinkle Cure Oil for mature skin

50ml Camelina Oil
29ml Macadamia Nut Oil
18ml/g Vitamin E Oil (undiluted)
2ml/g Vitamin A Palmitate
1ml/g Echium Seed CO_2 Extract
5 drops Rosemary Antioxidant (CO_2 Extract)

Shiny Hair Oil

For shinier hair. Camelina oil also gives the hair follicles a protective coating.
60ml Camelina Oil
20ml Jojoba Oil
15ml Calendula Oil
5ml/g Vitamin E Oil (undiluted)
5 drops Rosemary Antioxidant (CO_2 Extract)

Camelina Scar Tissue Treatment Oil

For general use. Apply up to twice a day.
40ml Camelina Oil
10ml Evening Primrose Oil
50ml/g Vitamin E Oil (undiluted)
10 drops Rosemary Antioxidant (CO_2 Extract)

Glossy Camelina Massage Oil

50ml Camelina Oil
30ml Jojoba Oil
15ml Castor Oil
5ml/g Vitamin E Oil (undiluted)
5 drops Rosemary Antioxidant (CO_2 Extract)

Percentages of Camelina Oil to use in products

Product	Product details	How much Oil you can use in the product	Average use
Skin Rejuvenation/ Anti-Wrinkle products	Creams	up to 15%	6-8%
	Face Oils	up to 75%	
	Rejuvenating Body Oils for all skin types	up to 50%	
Creams	Dry and Mature Skin	up to 10%	4-6%
	Oily Skin	up to 7%	5-6%
Acne Treatment products	Treatment Creams	up to 12%	6-8%
	Daily use Treatment Oils	up to 50%	
Eczema and Psoriasis products	Treatment Creams	up to 12%	7-8%
	Treatment Oils	up to 50%	
Treatment Oils	Scar Tissue Oil Blends	up to 40%	
	Bedsore Treatment Oils	up to 30%	
	Rheumatism/Arthritis Treatment Oils	up to 50%	
Hair Care products	Everyday use Hair Treatment Oils	up to 40%	
	Hair/Scalp Cure Oils	up to 80%	
Massage Oil Blends	All skin types	Up to 30% together with fattier, softer and longer Oils such as Sweet Almond and Jojoba.	

Table 14: Percentages of Camelina Oil to use in products

Castor Oil

Castor
INCI name: Ricinus communis

Description

The castor oil plant is a 5-10 metre high tree in the wild. When cultivated, it is a 2-3 metre high bush and it is found in many different varieties. These are grown in most of the world's temperate and warmer regions. The vegetable oil is extracted from the castor bean. It is a fatty, thick, sticky, liquid, stable oil, which doesn't go rancid easily and therefore keeps for a long time. Every fruit has three beans, which contain nearly 50% oil. One part of this oil is the very poisonous enzyme, ricin. This is a by-product after it has been pressed. The beans are usually fried or boiled before pressing to remove the ricin or the oil is heated after cold pressing, which also destroys the poison. Historically, castor oil has been used for therapeutic purposes since the advent of the Egyptian culture. When building the pyramids the workers used it for sun protection. In Egypt and China it was used as a cooking oil. Castor oil is used mostly today in western countries as a laxative in dosages of 15-20ml. As a lot of children can attest to, it doesn't have a pleasant taste due to its strong oily taste and texture. For use in natural skin care, it makes an excellent cleansing and drawing oil.

The SAP value for castor oil is 126-132g.

Absorption Note
Base.

Natural Vitamin Content
0.003%-004%, or 3-4mg per 100ml of castor oil of vitamin E (naturally-occurring d-alpha tocopherol).

Origin
China, India and Brazil.

Shelf Life
Keeps for 2-5 years.

Freezing Point
-15°C (+59°F).

Uses of Castor Oil

- Castor oil is different from other vegetable oils in that it can be blended and dispersed with 91% alcohol. Other vegetable oils cannot be dispersed with alcohol. Cold pressed castor oil is the raw material used to make turkey red oil (saponified castor oil).
- The oily surface of castor protects against weather and wind.
- It can be used in an oil-based perfume as a neutral fixative.
- Used in massage oil blends for whole body massage because the skin very slowly absorbs it. However, because it is short, sticky and resistant, you should use only a small percentage in your massage blends.
- Essential for inclusion in cleansing and peeling products as it draws dirt to itself.
- Good to use in ointments or creams which treat dry skin patches on elbows, knees and heels.
- Its cleansing properties make it an excellent addition to eczema and psoriasis treatment creams.
- It is absorbed very slowly by the skin and is therefore used for more refined coloured cosmetics such as lipsticks and in cleansing creams and other products where it is important that the oil does not become absorbed too quickly.
- It is used to add shine to lipsticks and other products where this is required. Also used to give the skin a sheen.
- In make-up remover products.
- In hair packs and hair oils you can use castor oil together with drier oils like jojoba. It makes the hair shiny and provides water protection.
- In the Ayurvedic therapeutic tradition in India it is heated and used as massage oil to treat back pain, rheumatism and itchiness.
- In India it is used to dress wounds and to treat skin infections.
- Castor oil makes very good cold processed soap and also makes the soap transparent.
- Many people have discovered that it is effective on age spots, brown pigment spots and liver spots. Apply neat three times daily for several months.
- Used as cooking oil in China.

Fatty Acid (Maximum) Content of Castor Oil

Please note, as the percentages below are for the maximum amount of fatty acid content found in castor oil, they may add up to more than 100%.

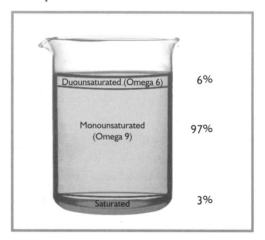

Breakdown of Fatty Acid content of Castor Oil	
Saturated	Palmitic Acid 1%
	Stearic Acid ≤2%
Mono-unsaturated	Ricinoleic Acid 75-90%
	Oleic Acid 2-7%
Duo-unsaturated	Linoleic Acid ≤6%

Castor Oil Sample Recipes

These Recipes make 100ml.

Castor Eye Make-up Remover Oil

48ml Castor Oil
50ml Almond Oil
2ml/g Vitamin E Oil (undiluted)

Method for Eye Make-up Remover
Apply this blend to the eyelids and wipe the area with cotton wool to remove the make-up.

Castor Cleansing Oil

50ml Castor Oil
40ml Apricot Kernel Oil
8ml Jojoba Oil
2ml/g Vitamin E Oil (undiluted)

Method for using Cleansing Oil
Apply this blend to the skin and wipe the area with cotton wool to remove the oil. The cleansing oil will remove the dirt from your skin.

A shiny smile

Gives a natural shine to your lips.
70ml Castor Oil
21ml Jojoba Oil
4g Carnauba Wax
5ml Pearlescent Colour of your choice

Method for a shiny smile
1) Melt the vegetable oils and the wax in a bain-marie, stirring all the while.
2) Cool down until it starts to thicken to a consistency of a thick soup.
3) Add colour/s and stir so that you have no lumps.
4) Pour into jars.

Castor Swedish Massage Oil

30ml Castor Oil
40ml Olive Oil
27ml Jojoba Oil
3ml/g Vitamin E Oil (undiluted)

Percentages of Castor Oil to use in products

Product	Product details	How much Oil you can use in the product	Average use
Products for dry skin patches on elbows, knees and heels	Creams	up to 10%	5-6%
	Ointments	up to 20%	12-15%
Skin Peeling and Cleansing products	Peeling Creams	up to 15%	5-10%
	Cleansing Lotions, Creams, Milks	up to 15%	5-10%
	Cleansing Oil Blends	up to 60%	40-50%
Eczema and Psoriasis Creams		up to 6%	2-4%

/contd

contd/

Product	Product details	How much Oil you can use in the product	Average use
Adding lubricating properties to a Massage Oil Blend		up to 15%	5-10%
Hair Packs and Hair Oils		Up to 30% - Remember to add drier Oils such as Jojoba to your Blend.	
Skin Treatment Oil	For reducing age, brown pigment and liver spots	100%	
Nappy Rash Treatment Oil Blends		up to 10%	
Make up products	Lipsticks	up to 80%	
	Make-up Remover products	up to 50%	45-50%

Table 15: Percentages of Castor Oil to use in products

Coconut Oil
(Liquid Fractionated)

Coconut
INCI name: Cocos nucifera

Description

Coconut butter is extracted from coconuts grown on palm trees, which are grown to a height of 20-25 metres in Asia. The fresh butter is pure white and retains that colour when it goes solid. It has a characteristic slightly sweet taste. Solid fatty acids have been removed from the coconut butter so that it becomes liquid coconut oil. Coconut in all of its forms is very important to one third of the world's population, who use it for food, soaps, cosmetics, hair oils, etc. Most massage practitioners and aromatherapists prefer the liquid fractionated coconut oil to the coconut butter as it has a lighter texture and long shelf life. Fractionated coconut oil is a fraction of the whole oil, in which most of the long-chain triglycerides are removed so that only saturated fats remain.

Because it is completely saturated, liquid fractionated coconut oil is even more heat stable than other forms of coconut oil and has a nearly indefinite shelf life. It is an odourless, non-oily, non-staining liquid oil that I believe should not be used by itself for skin care, but rather should be blended with cold pressed oils and vitamins. See page 3 for the 'Hardening of fats and oils'.

Liquid fractionated coconut oil gives softness and nourishment to skin and hair care products including hair dressings, soaps, sun care products, body oils and it adds body to massage products. Don't use in products for people with oily or large-pored skin as it may clog their pores.

The SAP value for coconut oil is 178-191g.

Absorption Note
Base.

Natural Vitamin Content
None that I know of.

Origin
Asia and the West Indies.

Shelf Life

Keeps for 4-5 years.

Freezing Point

-10°C (+14°F).

Contraindications for Coconut Oil

Due to the 100% solid fatty acid content, coconut oil should not be used on oily, large-pored or acne-prone skin, as it can further enlarge pores or clog them.

Uses of Coconut Oil

- Coconut oil is a very good emollient for skin care products.
- Excellent in hair conditioners in combination with castor oil.
- In hair packs for dry hair.
- It helps to increase hair growth when you have experienced hair loss.
- In the countries where coconuts are found, it is used for its beneficial hair care qualities, such as making the hair shiny and glossy.
- It promotes tanning. It has no natural sun filter, but it helps the skin to become brown.
- Because it is a long oil, it gives massage oils extra glide and lubrication so makes it excellent for whole body massage.
- Gives softness and lubricating properties to massage creams and lotions.
- You could use it as a bath oil on its own or if you would like the bath oil to have better dispersing qualities, then blend it with turkey red oil (saponified castor oil).
- Add to bath salts recipes as the main vegetable oil, but mix in with turkey red oil as well.

- It is absorbed slowly by the skin and has a soothing effect on sensitive and irritated skin.
- There are several studies that have indicated that the saturated fat in coconut oil is metabolised in the body in the same way as unsaturated fat and, as a result, low density lipoproteins (so-called "bad cholesterol") will not be increased due to the intake of coconut oil.
- Used in oil-based perfumes as the oil keeps well and is odourless.
- Due to its fattiness, it is also used in protective skin care products such as hand and foot creams or lotions, which protect the skin from the elements.
- Liquid fractionated coconut oil is also used in the making of commercially available massage oils, essences and many cosmetics.

Fatty Acid (Maximum) Content of Coconut Oil (Liquid Fractionated)

Please note, as the percentages in this illustration are for the maximum amount of fatty acid content found in coconut oil, they may add up to more than 100%.

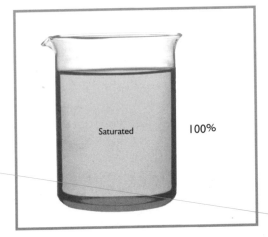

Saturated   100%

Breakdown of Fatty Acid content of Coconut Oil (Liquid Fractionated)	
Saturated	Caprylic Acid 55-75%
	Capricic Acid 25-45%
	Lauric Acid <3%
	Caproic Acid <2%
	Myristic Acid <1%

Coconut Oil Sample Recipes

These Recipes make 100ml.

Sun Oil (Before Sun)

30ml Coconut Oil, Liquid Fractionated
30ml Sesame Oil
30ml Sunflower Oil
10ml/g Vitamin E Oil (undiluted)
5 drops Rosemary Antioxidant (CO$_2$ Extract)

Swedish Massage Oil Recipe 1

34ml Coconut Oil, Liquid Fractionated
30ml Jojoba Oil
20ml Sweet Almond Oil
15ml Thistle Oil
1ml/g Vitamin E Oil (undiluted)

Swedish Massage Oil Recipe 2

This blend is ideal for sensitive skin.
40ml Coconut Oil, Liquid Fractionated
30ml Apricot Kernel Oil
20ml Jojoba Oil
9ml Camelina Oil
1ml/g Vitamin E Oil (undiluted)

Massage Oil for dry, sensitive skin

For Swedish massage/whole body massage.
35ml Coconut Oil, Liquid Fractionated
34ml Jojoba Oil
30ml Thistle Oil
1ml/g Vitamin E Oil (undiluted)

Coconut Sports Massage Oil Recipe 1

45ml Coconut Oil, Liquid Fractionated
15ml Jojoba Oil
5ml Thistle Oil
35ml/g Vitamin E Oil (undiluted)
10 drops Rosemary Antioxidant (CO$_2$ Extract)

Coconut Sports Massage Oil Recipe 2

35ml Coconut Oil, Liquid Fractionated
20ml Jojoba Oil
15ml Thistle Oil
5ml Borage Oil
25ml/g Vitamin E Oil (undiluted)
5 drops Rosemary Antioxidant (CO$_2$ Extract)

Shiny Hair Oil

35ml Coconut Oil, Liquid Fractionated
40ml Thistle Oil
20ml Calendula Oil
5ml/g Vitamin E Oil (undiluted)
5 drops Rosemary Antioxidant (CO$_2$ Extract)

Percentages of Coconut Oil to use in products

Product	Product details	How much Oil you can use in the product	Average use
Face Oils	Dry, mature, sensitive skin	up to 10%	
Body Oils	Dry, mature, sensitive skin	up to 50%	
Massage products for dry, mature/sensitive skin	Aromatherapy Oil Blends	Up to 50% - remember to blend with cold pressed Oils and with Vitamins.	
	Swedish Massage Oil Blends	Up to 50% - remember to blend with cold pressed Oils and with Vitamins.	20-30%
	Sports Massage Oil Blends	up to 60%	40-50%
	Massage Creams/Lotions	up to 50%	15-25%
Hair Packs	Dry Hair	up to 50%	
Skin Protection products	Hand Creams	Up to 15% - blend with Jojoba Oil.	10-12%
	Foot Creams	up to 15%	10-12%
Sun Care products	Sun Oils	up to 40%	25-30%

Table 16: Percentages of Coconut Oil to use in products

Comfrey Oil

Comfrey

INCI name: Symphytum officinalis and usually the INCI name for the oil that the comfrey is macerated in.

Description

Comfrey's name derives from the Latin *con firma*, i.e. 'with strength', from the belief that it could heal broken bones. Long used to heal wounds, comfrey leaves and roots have also been used to cure ailments ranging from stubborn leg ulcers to broken bones, hence its name 'boneset' or 'knitbone'. Since 400BCE early Greek physicians have used comfrey to stop bleeding, treat bronchial problems, heal wounds, and mend broken bones. Parts used are the roots and/or leaf, which are harvested during the growth cycle, but preferably not when in full flower.

Macerated comfrey oils are a deep green colour due to the allantoin content of the comfrey. The cell proliferant, allantoin, speeds growth, not only in human tissue, but the tissues in the comfrey plant itself. This means that comfrey grows very fast and can flower many times in a growing season if cut back. I suggest you always buy comfrey oil that has been macerated in a light oil such as sunflower as it will spread easily and be readily absorbed by the skin.

For the SAP value, refer to the vegetable oil that the comfrey is macerated in.

Natural Vitamin Content

Refer to the vegetable oil that the comfrey is macerated in. It varies from supplier to supplier.

Origin

Comfrey is grown all over the world, including the United Kingdom. During the Irish potato famine in the 1840s, an Englishman named Henry Doubleday became convinced that the world could be saved from hunger and suffering by using comfrey. He was so intrigued by its possibilities as a useful crop that he devoted the rest of his life to popularising it. The Henry Doubleday Research Association (HDRA), which still exists in England today, was set up in 1954 by Lawrence Hills, who in turn was inspired by Henry Doubleday and his introduction of Russian comfrey to the UK.

Shelf Life

Refer to the oil that the comfrey has been macerated in.

Freezing Point

Refer to the oil that the comfrey has been macerated in.

Contraindications. Important, please read before using Comfrey

- Do not use comfrey oil/products in any form when pregnant or breastfeeding.
- Do not use comfrey oil/products if you have a current or historical problem with your liver.
- Do not use this herb externally on new puncture wounds or deep cuts because the outer layers of skin will be stimulated by the comfrey to close and heal the outer layers of skin before there is time to drain and regenerate the deeper tissues. In these cases you can first apply calendula oil and once the swelling and pain have subsided and the wound is clean, drained and healing normally, comfrey oil may be safely applied to speed up the wound healing process effectively. **Note**: You may use a 20% solution of chamomile hydrolate in water to clean the wound.
- When using comfrey oil for post-operative clients, such as people who have had hip replacements it is VERY important to allow a period of 2-3 months before applying comfrey oil. This is to allow the deeper tissue to heal. You can use calendula oil in the first 2-3 months and then combine it or use comfrey oil on its own after this initial period.

Further information

- See page 29 for how to make an oil compress.

Fatty Acid (Maximum) Content of Comfrey Oil

Refer to the fatty acid illustration and breakdown table of the oil that the calendula has been macerated in.

Uses of Comfrey Oil

- Comfrey is mainly used externally to treat inflammation and to stimulate wound, bone fracture and, as some report, even cartilage healing.
- The important factor about comfrey for natural skin care, is that due to the high content of the phytochemical allantoin, it is a natural cell proliferant, so promotes the growth of new skin cells and helps sensitive skin to become more resilient, counteracting dryness and cracking. In addition, plants like comfrey, which have a high carbohydrate content, are considered to rejuvenate the skin and to have healing, soothing and moisture-retaining properties. This makes comfrey oil excellent for treating rough, damaged skin and can, with time, alleviate wrinkling and enable skin tissue to regain its youthful elasticity.
- It rebuilds damaged cell tissue or wounds caused by surgery, acne, eczema or psoriasis. It works well for these purposes in creams as well as in vegetable treatment oils and oil compresses.

- In creams, lotions and massage and treatment oils for treating sports injuries. It is excellent for aiding in the healing of torn muscles, ligaments, bruises, sprains and strains. Bruising results from the release of blood from the capillaries into the tissues under the skin. The characteristic bluish-black mark on the skin lightens in colour and eventually fades as the blood is absorbed by the tissues and carried away. Bruising usually occurs as a result of injury, but is occasionally spontaneous and an indication of an allergic reaction, or more serious disease. For whole body massage oils, remember to combine with longer oils such as jojoba, and oils with heating properties, such as castor oil.

- When making products containing comfrey oil, remember that comfrey and calendula oils are very synergistic in their effects, so you can add calendula oil or CO_2 extract to your products.

- In preparations for mature women, it assists in the treatment and prevention of osteoporosis.

- It is also used for treating: bone infections; general bodily aches and pains; sores which do not heal; varicose ulcers; varicose veins; and boils.

- Besides allantoin, comfrey also contains tannins, glycosides, mucilage, and is an excellent source of vitamin B12, very relevant in creams for vegetarians and vegans who may be short of this essential vitamin. It also contains vegetable protein.

Comfrey Oil Sample Recipes

These Recipes make 100ml.

Sports Massage Oil

A warming oil for the whole body.
30ml Comfrey Oil
20ml Avocado Oil
25ml Jojoba Oil
10ml Castor Oil
5ml Calendula Oil
10ml/g Vitamin E Oil (undiluted)
5 drops Rosemary Antioxidant (CO_2 Extract)

Sports Treatment Oil

For treating torn muscles and ligaments.
60ml Comfrey Oil
8ml Calendula Oil
30ml/g Vitamin E Oil (undiluted)
2ml/g Chamomile CO_2 Extract
5 drops Rosemary Antioxidant (CO_2 Extract)

Bruised Skin Treatment Oil

60ml Comfrey Oil
20ml St. John's Wort Oil
10ml Arnica Oil
9ml/g Vitamin E Oil (undiluted)
1ml/g Calendula CO_2 Extract
5 drops Rosemary Antioxidant (CO_2 Extract)

How to use

Apply neat 2-3 times a day. This blend could also be used in an oil compress and applied 2-3 times a day. See page 29 for the method.

Tip

This blend is ideal to have already mixed if you have children in the house.

Everyday Comfrey Acne Treatment Oil

20ml Comfrey Oil
60ml Rosehip Oil
16ml/g Vitamin E Oil (undiluted)
2ml/g Calendula CO_2 Extract
2ml/g Vitamin A Palmitate
5 drops Rosemary Antioxidant (CO_2 Extract)

Sports Injury Compress

Use for sports injuries such as torn muscles and ligaments. Use up to 100% comfrey oil or up to 80% of the oil and combine with other oils, tinctures, botanical CO_2 extracts and essential oils. I recommend arnica oil, St. John's wort oil and essential oils such as lavender and/or chamomile essential oils for pain relief. See the 'Method for oil compresses' on page 29.

Fractures/Broken Bone Treatment Oil

Don't ever use on open wounds. However, if the skin is not broken, you can use this on recently fractured or broken bones and on wounds.

80ml Comfrey Oil
6ml Calendula Oil
4ml Arnica Oil
10ml/g Vitamin E Oil (undiluted)
5 drops Rosemary Antioxidant (CO_2 Extract)

How to use Fractures/Broken Bone Treatment Oil

Apply liberally or make an oil compress and apply once a day. See page 29 for the method.

Skin and Tissue Repair Treatment Oil

50ml Comfrey Oil
30ml Rosehip Oil
16ml/g Vitamin E Oil (undiluted)
2ml/g Sea Buckthorn CO_2 Extract
2ml/g Vitamin A Palmitate
5 drops Rosemary Antioxidant (CO_2 Extract)

How to use Skin and Tissue Repair Treatment Oil

Apply liberally or make an oil compress and apply once a day. See page 29 for the method.

Scar Tissue Healing Oil

50ml Comfrey Oil
47ml/g Vitamin E Oil (undiluted)
2ml/Sea Buckthorn CO_2 Extract
1ml/g Calendula CO_2 Extract
·10 drops Rosemary Antioxidant (CO_2 Extract)

How to use Scar Tissue Healing Oil

This oil can be used to heal scars, including keloid scars. Use twice a day on old scar tissue. You need 2-3 months to see a result. **NB** Do not use on open scars! See 'Contraindications'.

Anti-Wrinkle/Skin Rejuvenation Face Oil

20ml Comfrey Oil
60ml Rosehip Oil
20ml/g Vitamin E Oil (undiluted)
5 drops Rosemary Antioxidant (CO_2 Extract)

Percentages of Comfrey Oil to use in products

Product	Product details	How much Oil you can use in the product	Average use
Soothing, Healing and Skin Protection products	Healing Creams	up to 15%	10-12%
	Soothing and Protective Hand Creams for counteracting dryness and cracked skin.	Up to 12% - add Jojoba Oil for its protective qualities.	6-8%
	Soothing and Healing Foot Creams for counteracting dryness and cracked skin on the feet.	up to 15%	10-12%
Skin Rejuvenation/ Anti-Wrinkle products	Creams	up to 10%	4-5%
	Face Oils	up to 25%	
Sports products	Sports Whole Body Massage Oil	up to 40%	
	Sports Injury Treatment Oil	Up to 60% - remember to combine with 'longer' Oils such as Jojoba, and Castor Oil for heating properties.	
	Compresses	up to 100%	
Bruised Skin Treatment products *I recommend that you combine Arnica Macerated Oil or Tincture as well as St. John's Wort Macerated Oil with Comfrey Oil for treating bruised skin.*	Treatment Oils	up to 80%	
	Ointments	up to 70%	
	Creams	up to 20%	15-17%
	Compresses	up to 80%	
Fractures/Broken Bones Treatment products	Treatment Oils	Up to 90% - beneficial to blend with a little Arnica if there is bruising and swollenness. You can also add Vitamin E Oil to aid the healing process.	

/contd

78

contd/

Product	Product details	How much Oil you can use in the product	Average use
Fractures/Broken Bones Treatment products *contd*	Compresses	Up to 90% - combine with Arnica and Vitamin E Oil. The most effective Comfrey Compresses are made with a Comfrey Root Decoction. For further information on how to make the decoction, see *The Aromantic Guide to the use of Herbs in Skin, Hair and Health Care products.*	
Products that repair tissue damage resulting from flesh wounds, chapped skin, sores, cracked skin, varicose veins, bunions, sprains, and burns. **NB** See Contraindications!	Creams	up to 20%	12-15%
	Ointments	up to 70%	
	Treatment Oils	up to 70%	
	Compresses	up to 70%	
Scar Tissue Treatment products **NB** See Contraindications	Keloid Scar Treatment Oils	Up to 70% - add Vitamin E to the Blend.	
	Treatment Oils for treating old and new scars	Up to 50% - add up to 50% (undiluted) Vitamin E Oil to the Blend. You will need to use it for 2-3 months for it to be effective.	
	Post-operative Scar Treatment Oils	Up to 60% - **NB** See Contraindications!	
Eczema and Psoriasis Treatment products	Treatment Creams	up to 15%	8-10%
	Treatment Oils	up to 35%	
Acne Treatment products	Treatment Creams	up to 10%	5-6%
	Daily Use Acne Treatment Oils	up to 30%	
Massage Oils		up to 20%	

Table 17: Percentages of Comfrey Macerated Oil to use in products

Evening Primrose Oil

Evening Primrose
INCI name: Oenothera biennis

Description

Evening primrose oil is cold pressed from the seeds of the evening primrose flower and is a dry, thin oil that is easily absorbed by the skin. The oil contains a very different ratio of fatty acids and a high quantity of gamma linolenic acid (GLA), which is a very rare fatty acid found in evening primrose oil (8-12%), borage oil (16-24%) blackcurrant seed oil (approximately 6%). Gamma linolenic acid (GLA) is a duounsaturated fatty acid closely related to the essential fatty acid, linoleic acid. Both are substances the body needs to create prostaglandins.

Evening primrose is very well researched. Gamma linolenic acid has been shown to have favourable effects on a number of disorders. It is taken internally to relieve premenstrual problems, alcohol withdrawal symptoms, high blood pressure, rheumatoid arthritis, hyperactivity in children, diabetes, atopical eczema (chronic, itching eczema) and multiple sclerosis. Evening primrose oil penetrates down and into the skin, which as a result becomes softer and is less prone to eczema and acne. It has a moisture-retaining effect, prevents drying of the skin, increases the cells' ability to absorb oxygen and to withstand disease. Evening primrose oil and other oils containing GLA are not a miracle cure but can help to support the body's own functioning to maintain good health. Borage oil is often used in preference to evening primrose oil as it is said to have a much higher (16-24%) GLA level. However, it is important to be aware that all the research on GLA carried out to date has been on evening primrose oil and it has even been registered in some countries as a medicine.

The SAP value for evening primrose oil is 136g.

Absorption Note

Top.

Natural Vitamin Content

Traces of vitamin E can be found in the oil.

Origin

Evening primrose is native to North America, where it grows wild. It was brought to Europe in the 1700s and now grows wild in the middle of Europe.

Shelf Life

Due to the high content of gamma linolenic acid you should never buy evening primrose oil that does not have added vitamin E oil or other natural antioxidants, otherwise it will go rancid within 6 months. Adding 0.5% undiluted vitamin E oil, or an equivalent antioxidant, will increase the shelf life to 2 years.

Freezing Point

-10°C (+14°F).

Further information

- See page 9 for more information about 'Prostaglandins'.
- See page 9 for 'Gamma linolenic acid and its function in the body'.
- See Table 6 on page 33 for 'How to choose between borage oil and evening primrose oil'.
- See 'Tips for buying borage, camelina, evening primrose, hemp seed, kiwi seed and rosehip oils' on page 29.

Uses of Evening Primrose Oil

- Evening primrose oil is a short oil that is quickly absorbed by the skin and does not leave an oily feeling on the skin and this makes it excellent for a face or skin oil. However, as it is a short oil it would not work well for a stand-alone massage oil that is used for long strokes (as in whole body massage). For this purpose, blend it with longer oils, such as jojoba oil.
- Due to the fact that evening primrose is a softer oil than borage oil, I would recommend evening primrose oil rather than borage oil for sensitive skin types or products.
- Anti-wrinkle/skin rejuvenation face oils and serums.
- Oil blends for healing scar tissue and wounds.
- In products that treat skin infections such as eczema, psoriasis and acne.
- In hair packs for treating dandruff.
- In wound-healing products.
- Always mix it with other vegetable oils for skin application, as it is too dry to use on its own.
- The oil can be taken internally by pouring it into a teaspoon first (as an alternative to capsules).

Fatty Acid (Maximum) Content of Evening Primrose Oil

Please note, as the percentages in this illustration are for the maximum amount of fatty acid content found in evening primrose oil, they may add up to more than 100%.

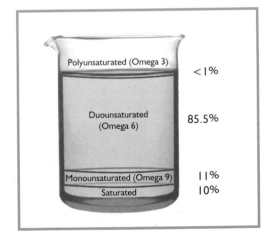

Breakdown of Fatty Acid content of Evening Primrose Oil	
Saturated	Palmitic Acid 6-7% Stearic Acid 1-3%
Mono-unsaturated	Oleic Acid 8-11%
Duo-unsaturated	Linoleic Acid 70-75% Gamma Linolenic Acid (GLA) 8-10.5%
Poly-unsaturated	Alpha Linoleic Acid <1%

Evening Primrose Oil Sample Recipes

Use these anti-wrinkle/skin rejuvenation face oils/serums in the morning and the evening. The Recipes make 100ml.

Anti-Wrinkle/Skin Rejuvenation Face Oil/Serum for dry skin

55ml Evening Primrose Oil

18ml Thistle Oil

25ml/g Vitamin E Oil (undiluted)

2ml/g Arctic Cranberry Seed Oil CO_2 Extract

5 drops Rosemary Antioxidant (CO_2 Extract)

Anti-wrinkle/Skin Rejuvenation Face Oil/Serum for mature skin

40ml Evening Primrose Oil

24ml Thistle Oil

10ml Macadamia Nut Oil

25ml/g Vitamin E Oil (undiluted)

1ml/g Echium CO_2 Extract

5 drops Rosemary Antioxidant (CO_2 Extract)

Anti-Wrinkle/Skin Rejuvenation Face Oil/Serum for sensitive skin

30ml Evening Primrose Oil

40ml Rosehip Oil

5ml Pumpkin Seed Oil

25ml/g Vitamin E Oil (undiluted)

5 drops Rosemary Antioxidant (CO_2 Extract)

Anti-Wrinkle/Skin Rejuvenation Face Oil/Serum for oily/large-pored skin

58ml Evening Primrose Oil

20ml Rosehip Oil

5ml Pumpkin Seed Oil

15ml/g Vitamin E Oil (undiluted)

2ml/g Sea Buckthorn CO_2 Extract

5 drops Rosemary Antioxidant (CO_2 Extract)

Scar Tissue Oil

35ml Evening Primrose Oil

15ml Rosehip Oil

50ml Vitamin E Oil (undiluted)

10 drops Rosemary Antioxidant (CO_2 Extract)

Baby Oil (everyday use)

50ml Evening Primrose Oil

20ml Shea Butter Oil

18ml Apricot Kernel Oil

10ml Kiwi Seed Oil

2ml/g Vitamin E Oil (undiluted)

Percentages of Evening Primrose Oil to use in products

Product	Product details	How much Oil you can use in the product	Average use
Face and Body Oils	Oily/large-pored skin	up to 60%	
	Dry/mature skin	up to 40%	
	Sensitive skin	up to 40%	
Anti-Wrinkle Face Oils and Serums	All skin types	up to 60%	
GLA Creams	For dry, mature and sensitive skin types	up to 10%	5-10%
	For oily/large-pored skin	up to 8%	5-7%
Eye Contour products	Creams	up to 10%	5-8%
	Oil Blends	up to 40%	
Baby products	Creams	up to 10%	5-7%
	Everyday Baby Oils	up to 30%	20-25%
	Treatment Oils	up to 40%	25-30%
Eczema & Psoriasis products	Treatment Creams	up to 20%	5-10%
	Treatment Oils	up to 30%	25-30%
Acne Treatment products	Creams	up to 15%	8-10%
	Treatment Oils	up to 35%	20-25%
Scar Tissue/Post-Surgery Treatment Oils		up to 35%	20-25%
Oil Blends that help wound healing		Up to 40% - combine with Vitamin E Oil (undiluted) and Comfrey Oil.	
Hair Treatment products	Hair Packs treating dandruff	up to 40%	
Massage Oil Blends	Dry/mature/sensitive skin	up to 20%	5-10%
	Oily/large-pored skin	up to 30%	10-15%

Table 18: Percentages of Evening Primrose Oil to use in products

Grape Seed Oil

Grape
INCI name: Vitis vinifera

Description

Grape seed oil is a clear, light yellow or green colour and is thin and dry. The classic body oil, it is pressed from the seeds of various varieties of grapes and is a by-product of wine making, which technically makes it a fruit (rather than a vegetable) oil. Almost all (98%) commercially available grape seed oil is extracted with the solvent hexane, which yields a high quantity of oil. The hexane is separated and I wouldn't consider this oil dangerous to use. The only alternative is to buy organic grape seed oil, which is in the same price range as borage oil. As grape seed oil is usually cheap and used in large quantities as a base or carrier oil, I doubt very much that the majority of people would pay for the expensive organic oil. For skin care it is best blended with cold pressed oils and is good for all skin types. Grape seed oil is high in linoleic acid (omega 6). Linoleic acid is an essential fatty acid, which helps to reduce the size of skin pores, so is excellent for normalising large-pored skin. Linoleic acid is also part of the cascade process for making prostaglandins that takes place in the body in order to regulate body processes such as inflammation and blood clotting.

The SAP value for grape seed oil is 126-136g.

Absorption Note

Top.

Natural Vitamin Content

0.016-0.027%, or 16-27mg per 100ml of grape seed oil of vitamin E (naturally-occurring d-alpha tocopherol).

Origin

Mainly from Italy but also from wine-producing countries such as France, Spain and Switzerland.

Shelf Life

2-3 years.

Freezing Point

-5°C (+23°F).

Further information

- See page 9 for more information about 'Gamma linolenic acid' and 'Prostaglandins'.
- See page 7 for 'More information on Essential Fatty Acids (Vitamin F)'.
- See page 29 for how to make an oil compress.

Uses of Grape Seed Oil

- Grape seed oil has a high content of linoleic acid (omega 6) which is an essential fatty acid because it cannot be manufactured by the body and must therefore be obtained from food or through the skin every day. The best quality is cold pressed and organic, rather than the more commonly used refined grape seed oil.

- The linoleic acid helps and relieves problems with poor blood circulation in feet and legs. This poor circulation can result in cramps, swollen feet or legs, discolouring, pain, leg ulcers, broken nails, etc.

- Grape seed oil is a neutral oil that most people can use without any adverse reactions. You can use grape seed oil or thistle oil to enhance the circulation. It is easier and cheaper to obtain cold pressed and organic thistle oil than it is to get cold pressed and organic grape seed oil. The enhanced circulation that results from the oil pack treatment shows in a number of ways: the feet and legs will regain normal temperature levels; discolouring and pain disappears; cold feet can become warm after just one night's oil pack (see recipes), itchiness after three days' oil application, leg ulcers and blemishes, as well as itching scars, can disappear or be much better after a week's treatment; pain can disappear after a month. If you want to treat chapped skin at the same time, add 2% calendula CO_2 extract or 10-15% macerated calendula oil. If you have problems with sweaty feet, athlete's foot, or smelly feet, add 2-3% (50-75 drops) of tea tree essential oil plus 0.5% (10-12 drops per 100ml of recipe) of lavender essential oil. Don't use the oil pack every night but interchange it with a warm foot bath every other night, using rosemary, pine and juniper essential oils, which enhance circulation.

- It has traditionally been used by massage therapists and aromatherapists as the main carrier, or base, oil.

- Makes an excellent base oil for massage as it is a long oil and so offers excellent lubricating qualities.

- It is a dry oil, which should never be used on its own as most of the grape seed oil on the market today is refined. It is, however, easy to massage into the skin and helps to enhance the skin's ability to absorb other raw materials added to the blend. In addition, it doesn't leave an oily feeling on the skin. All of these qualities make it excellent for massage oils.

- Many people blend it with refined almond oil, which is cheap to buy, but limited in its effect on the skin. I recommend that grape seed oil is blended with cold pressed fattier oils such as apricot kernel, sweet almond or avocado for better lubrication as well as skin nourishment.

- Refined grape seed oil is not recommended for creams and lotions as high quality cold pressed oils such as thistle or sunflower oil are preferable for this purpose. If the oil is still too rough, add some smooth oils such as sweet almond or apricot kernel oil.

- Although suitable for all skin types, grape seed is particularly good for use on oily or large-pored skin; acne-prone skin; or thin, sensitive or damaged skin that results from the topical use of cortisone treatments. Skin atrophy (which is from the Greek *atrophia*, meaning lack of nourishment) is a skin condition resulting from the use of corticosteroid creams or hydrocortisone products. Acute and extreme cases of skin atrophy can result in the thinning of the top two layers of skin, the dermis and epidermis, causing a depression in the skin. Grape seed oil can improve this condition after a few weeks of applying it and the condition will usually disappear in a few months of applying the oil. Even though the refined grape seed oil would work for treating these conditions, the organic and cold pressed variety would obviously be more effective. However, due to its high cost and relative unavailability, I would personally recommend using organic and cold pressed thistle oil instead, which is far cheaper and more easily available.

- Apply to finger- or toe- nails for increased circulation and nourishment. The oil treatments will help heal brittle nails that tend to split easily.

- Grape seed oil is also used for culinary purposes. It is a thin and dry oil with a very mild flavour and therefore good for salad dressings as it will not overpower the other ingredients. It can easily be combined with other stronger flavoured and more expensive oils. Refined grape seed has a high smoke point (over 200°C/392°F) and can therefore be heated.

Fatty Acid (Maximum) Content of Grape Seed Oil

Please note, as the percentages in this illustration are for the maximum amount of fatty acid content found in grape seed oil, they may add up to more than 100%.

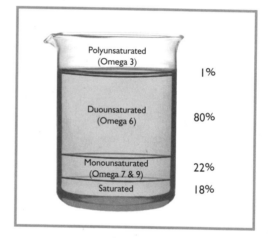

Breakdown of Fatty Acid content of Grape Seed Oil	
Saturated	Palmitic Acid 5-11%
	Stearic Acid 3-6%
	Arachidic Acid <1%
Mono-unsaturated	Oleic Acid 12-20%
	Palmitoleic Acid <1%
	Gadoleic Acid <1%
Duo-unsaturated	Linoleic Acid 58-80%
Poly-unsaturated	Alpha Linolenic Acid ≤1%

Grape Seed Oil Sample Recipes

These Recipes make 100ml.

Massage Oil Blend for dry and sensitive skin

32ml Grape Seed Oil

32ml Sweet Almond Oil, cold pressed

31ml Apricot Kernel Oil

5ml/g Vitamin E Oil (undiluted)

5 drops Rosemary Antioxidant (CO_2 Extract)

Massage Oil Blend for dry and mature skin

25ml Grape Seed Oil

40ml Macadamia Nut Oil

30ml Jojoba Oil

5ml/g Vitamin E Oil (undiluted)

5 drops Rosemary Antioxidant (CO_2 Extract)

Massage Oil Blend for oily/large-pored skin

68ml Grape Seed oil

20ml Thistle Oil

10ml Jojoba Oil

2ml/g Vitamin E Oil (undiluted)

Nourishing Skin Oil for after-hydrocortisone treatment

35ml Grape Seed Oil

20ml Thistle Oil

27ml Borage Oil

15ml/g Vitamin E Oil (undiluted)

1ml/g Vitamin A Palmitate

1ml/g Calendula CO_2 Extract

1ml/g Sea Buckthorn CO_2 Extract

5 drops Rosemary Antioxidant (CO_2 Extract)

Skin and Massage Oil/Oil Pack Blend for increased circulation

50ml Grape Seed Oil

25ml Avocado Oil

25ml/g Vitamin E Oil (undiluted)

5 drops Rosemary Antioxidant (CO_2 Extract)

Method

1) Soak two cotton socks in a bowl of the oil blend shown in the recipe above.

2) Squeeze a little of the oil out of the socks so that they are not dripping.

3) Put the socks on your feet and cover both feet with plastic bags.

4) Finally, cover the plastic bags with larger, dry socks.

5) Keep on overnight and remove in morning.

6) Repeat every other night, alternating with a warm foot bath containing essential oils that increase circulation (see 'uses of grape seed oil' for more information).

Brittle Nail Treatment Oil

40ml Grape Seed Oil

40ml Sesame Seed Oil

10ml Rice Bran Oil

10ml/g Vitamin E Oil (undiluted)

5 drops Rosemary Antioxidant (CO_2 Extract)

Eye Oil

For use on the sensitive skin around the eyes.

35ml Grape Seed Oil

60ml Rosehip Oil

4ml/g Vitamin E Oil (undiluted)

1ml/g Vitamin A Palmitate

Percentages of Grape Seed Oil to use in products

Product	Product details	How much Oil you can use in the product	Average use
Massage Oil Blends	Swedish Massage Oils for all skin types	up to 40%	
	For increased circulation	up to 50%	
	For oily/large pore conditions or for skin that needs an Oil that has good lubrication qualities	up to 70%	
Face Oils	Nourishing properties	up to 20%	
Nail Oils	Treatment Oils	up to 40%	
Products that treat circulation problems	Leg Oils	up to 40%	
	Foot Oil Packs	up to 100%	
Post-Cortisone use Nourishing Skin Oils		Up to 40% - always add Gamma Linolenic Acid- and Vitamin-rich Oils to this Blend.	
Acne Treatment Oil Blends		up to 20%	

Table 19: Percentages of Grape Seed Oil to use in products

Hazelnut Oil

Hazelnut

INCI name: Corylus avellana

Description

Hazelnut is a small deciduous tree that grows up to 6 metres high with shrubby, dark stems. The tree likes cool forest areas with nutrient-rich soils. The leaves are ovate with serrated edges and the male flowers are yellowish catkins whilst the female flowers are deep red. The male and female flowers are both on the same tree. Hazelnut oil is produced from the nut kernels that contain 40-50% oil, which is a light golden to yellow-brown with a sweet, nutty flavour. Hazelnut produces a very nourishing, versatile and astringent oil that is particularly suitable for sensitive, baby or mature skin types. The cold pressed oil is the best quality.

The SAP value for hazelnut oil is 136-139g.

Absorption Note

Middle.

Natural Vitamin Content

0.04%, or 40mg per 100ml of hazelnut oil of vitamin E (naturally-occurring d-alpha tocopherol).

Origin

There are significant commercial orchards in France, Germany, Turkey Iran and Caucasus as well as the Pacific northwest region of United States and Canada.

Shelf Life

3-4 years.

Freezing Point

Under -20°C (-2°F).

Contraindications/warnings

Check for nut allergies with client.

Further information

- See page 15 for 'Rebalancing certain skin types with certain vegetable oils'.
- See page 29 for how to make an oil compress.

Uses of Hazelnut Oil

- It nourishes, softens, and protects the skin as well being astringent and stimulating to the circulation.

- When using this oil in your recipes, it is quite a good idea to blend with neutral smelling oils such as refined sweet almond oil as the hazelnut oil has a nutty aroma.

- Hazelnut oil is close to sweet almond in the sense of how it feels on the skin but is much drier. We consider sweet almond a fatty oil, whereas hazelnut is half-dry. Both are soft, long and smooth. They contain nearly exactly the same proportions of fatty acids. Because of these similarities, hazelnut oil is often used as substitute for sweet almond oil.

- Easily absorbed by the skin without leaving a greasy residue.

- Because it has a low freezing point of under -20°C (-2°F) and because it is fairly astringent, it works well for treating oily and combination skin and can even balance this type of skin to normal. For this purpose, blend smaller quantities of the hazelnut oil with rosehip oil and squalane.

- Because of hazelnut's soft and smooth qualities, it is ideal for including in baby products.

- Suits dry, sensitive, normal, oily and mature skin but is especially suitable for sensitive skin types.

- Excellent addition to acne treatment blends due to its astringent effect. Blend with drier oils for this purpose.

- A good skin care oil for dry, irritated skin but blend with other oils to combat the astringency.

- Combine with neutral smelling refined sweet almond in massage creams and lotions.

- Can be used on its own or in blends or products for face and body care.

- A natural sun filter.

- Encourages cell regeneration and tones and firms the skin, so useful for thread veins.

- Due to the high content of monounsaturated fatty acids it has good lubricating properties and is a long oil. This makes hazelnut oil excellent for use in whole body massage.

- In hair packs and hair treatment blends. Crushed hazelnuts were traditionally used in Sweden as a hair compress to aid hair growth.

- A good digestive oil for salad dressings. Also excellent for cooking and frying as it has a high smoke point of +221°C/429.8°F.

- Internally it is recommended for adolescents, the elderly, and pregnant women (unless of course they have nut allergies!).

Fatty Acid (Maximum) Content of Hazelnut Oil

Please note, as the percentages in this illustration are for the maximum amount of fatty acid content found in hazelnut oil, they may add up to more than 100%.

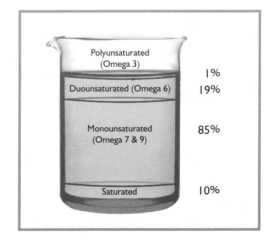

Polyunsaturated (Omega 3)	1%
Duounsaturated (Omega 6)	19%
Monounsaturated (Omega 7 & 9)	85%
Saturated	10%

Breakdown of Fatty Acid content of Hazelnut Oil	
Saturated	Palmitic Acid 4-6%
	Stearic Acid 1-3%
	Myristic Acid <0.2%
	Arachidic Acid <1%
Mono-unsaturated	Oleic Acid 70-84%
	Palmitoleic Acid <0.2%
Duo-unsaturated	Linoleic Acid 9-19%
Poly-unsaturated	Alpha Linolenic Acid <1%

Hazelnut Oil Sample Recipes

These Recipes make 100ml.

Baby Oil for everyday use

30ml Hazelnut Oil
30ml Sweet Almond Oil, refined
25ml Shea Butter Oil
13ml Rosehip Oil
2ml/g Vitamin E Oil (undiluted)

Dry Leg Oil

30ml Hazelnut Oil
30ml Sweet Almond Oil, refined
20ml Thistle Oil
8ml Calendula Oil
6ml Shea Butter Oil
5ml/g Vitamin E Oil (undiluted)
1ml/g Sea Buckthorn CO_2 Extract
5 drops Rosemary Antioxidant (CO_2 Extract)

Hazelnut Before Sun Oil

40ml Hazelnut Oil
20g Coconut Butter (melt in bain-marie first, then add to the blend)
20ml Sesame Oil
10ml Sunflower Oil
10ml/g Vitamin E Oil (undiluted)
5 drops Rosemary Antioxidant (CO_2 Extract)

Hazelnut Anti-Wrinkle Cure Oil for dry, mature and/or sensitive skin

30ml Hazelnut Oil
20ml Sweet Almond Oil, refined
20ml Evening Primrose or Borage Oil
10ml Thistle Oil
20ml/g Vitamin E Oil (undiluted)
5 drops Rosemary Antioxidant (CO_2 Extract)

Hazelnut Acne Treatment Oil

For everyday use.
20ml Hazelnut Oil
20ml Evening Primrose
20ml Thistle Oil
10ml Rosehip Oil
10ml Jojoba Oil
15ml/g Vitamin E Oil (undiluted)
2ml/g Vitamin A Palmitate
1.5ml Aromantic's Anti-Acne Formula
1ml/g Sea Buckthorn CO_2 Extract
0.5ml/g Chamomile CO_2 Extract
5 drops Rosemary Antioxidant (CO_2 Extract)

Hazelnut Swedish Massage Oil for dry or sensitive skin

35ml Hazelnut Oil
35ml Peach Kernel Oil
20ml Thistle Oil, refined
7ml Evening Primrose Oil
3ml/g Vitamin E Oil (undiluted)

Hazelnut Swedish Massage Oil for dry skin

30ml Hazelnut Oil
15ml Sweet Almond Oil, refined
15ml Coconut Butter (melt in bain-marie first, then add to the blend)
20ml Jojoba Oil
18ml Olive Oil
2ml/g Vitamin E Oil (undiluted)

Percentages of Hazelnut Oil to use in products

Product	Product details	How much Oil you can use in the product	Average use
Face Oils & Serums	All skin types	up to 20%	
Body Oils	All skin types	up to 30%	
Massage products	Massage Oils (all skin types)	up to 50%	
	Massage Creams and Lotions	up to 30%	15-20%
Acne Treatment products	Treatment Creams	up to 10%	5-6%
	Daily use Acne Treatment Oils	up to 25%	10-15%
Hair Treatment products	Oil Blends and Packs	up to 50%	
Creams	All skin types	up to 10%	5-6%
	Oily skin	3-4%	
Baby products	Creams	up to 12%	5-8%
	Everyday Baby Oils	up to 40%	
	Treatment Oils	up to 50%	
Skin Cleansing products	Creams and Lotions	Up to 30% - remember to add Castor Oil to the Recipe.	10-15%
Sun Care products	Sun Creams	up to 15%	10-12%
	Sun Oils	up to 40%	

Table 20: Percentages of Hazelnut Oil to use in products

Hemp Seed Oil

Hemp
INCI name: Cannabis sativa

Description

A thin, very dry oil, green yellow to strong green in colour. Over time it becomes brown-yellow to brown-green and acquires more flavour and smell. Hemp seed oil is produced by cold pressing the hemp seed and the oil comprises 25%-35% of the total seed weight. The seed of the of the hemp plant is not really a true seed, but an "achene", a fruit containing the seed in a case or covering. Linoleic acid and alpha linolenic acid usually account for approximately 50-80% and 15-25% respectively, of the total fatty acid content found in hemp seed oil. This 3:1 balance between the two essential fatty acids has been claimed optimal for human nutrition (Erasmus, 1993) and is apparently unique among the common plant oils, although blackcurrant seed oil is close to this figure. It also contains up to 13% omega 9 fatty acids. Whole hemp seed contains approximately 20-25% protein, 20-30% carbohydrates and 10-15% insoluble fibre, as well as minerals, particularly phosphorous, potassium, magnesium, sulphur and calcium, along with modest amounts of iron and zinc. It is also a fair source of carotene, a vitamin A precursor. Hemp seed oil does not contain significant amounts of the psychoactive substance, tetrahydrocannabinol (THC), which is found in marijuana (hemp leaves) for THC to be active in hemp seed oil. Hemp seed oil is suitable for all skin types.

The SAP value for hemp seed oil is 135-137g.

Absorption Note

Top.

Natural Vitamin Content

0.0003%, or 0.3mg per 100ml of hemp seed oil of vitamin E (naturally-occurring d-alpha tocopherol).

Origin

Now grown all over the world. Canada is very active in its commercial production.

Shelf Life

Due to the high content of polyunsaturated fatty acids you should never buy hemp seed oil that does not have added vitamin E oil or other natural antioxidants, otherwise it will go rancid within 6 months. Adding 0.5% undiluted vitamin E oil, or an equivalent antioxidant, will increase the shelf life to 2 years.

Freezing Point

Under -20°C (-2°F).

Further information

- See page 9 for more information about prostaglandins.
- See page 9 for 'Gamma linolenic acid and its function in the body'.
- See page 15 for 'Rebalancing certain skin types with certain vegetable oils'.
- See page 29 for 'Tips for buying borage, camelina, evening primrose, hemp seed, kiwi seed and rosehip oils'.

Uses of Hemp Seed Oil

- Now that there is a resurgence of interest in this versatile plant, it is grown in a number of countries for clothing, textiles, food, paper, rope, building materials and of course oil and the plant can even be used to produce plastics and petrochemical substitutes and used for energy production. The oil can be eaten on its own, blended into other body care and food products or used as a lubricant.
- The oil contains 2-3% GLA (gamma linolenic acid) and can be used in the same way as evening primrose oil and borage oil. The body converts the GLA to prostaglandins. The skin needs prostaglandins and deficiencies will cause dryness, loss of suppleness and wrinkling. The skin will age more quickly and be less tolerant to sunlight and any damage to the skin will take longer to heal. Hemp seed oil penetrates down and into the skin, which as a result becomes softer and is less prone to eczema, psoriasis and acne. It has a moisture-retaining effect, prevents drying of the skin, and increases the cells' ability to absorb oxygen and to withstand disease.
- The GLA content makes it ideal for use in eczema, psoriasis and acne treatment products.
- Because it absorbs deeply and rapidly, it leaves little residue on the skin surface, which makes it effective in enhancing the skin's ability to absorb other active raw materials added to the hemp seed blend.
- Skin care products containing hemp seed oil can reduce skin discomfort by soothing and restoring dry or damaged skin and increasing the natural moisture-retention capacity.
- With regular use, skin care products containing the oil can help slow down the effects of skin aging and leave the skin smooth, soft and moisturised.
- When used in hair care products, hemp seed oil imparts gloss and manageability to hair and can bring relief from dry scalp or hair damage caused by blow-dryer heat, chemical perms, hair colouring or sunlight.
- Works well when used in hair packs in combination with jojoba oil.
- Don't use 100% hemp seed oil in your massage oil blends as it is a short oil, and very, very dry and rough for whole body massage but more suitable for face oils, which require

short strokes to massage it into the skin. Whether for massage or facial oils, blend with smoother, softer oils

- If used on sensitive skin, it is very important that you add smoother, longer, oils such as rosehip, and smoother, longer and fattier oils such as avocado and apricot kernel oils.

Fatty Acid (Maximum) Content of Hemp Seed Oil

Please note, as the percentages in this illustration are for the maximum amount of Fatty Acid content found in hemp seed oil, they may add up to more than 100%.

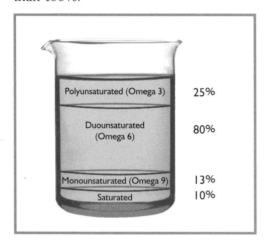

Polyunsaturated (Omega 3)	25%
Duounsaturated (Omega 6)	80%
Monounsaturated (Omega 9)	13%
Saturated	10%

Breakdown of Fatty Acid content of Hemp Seed Oil	
Saturated	Palmitic Acid 5-6%
	Stearic Acid 2%
	Arachidic Acid 1-2%
Mono-unsaturated	Oleic Acid 12-13%
Duo-unsaturated	Linoleic Acid 55-77%
	Gamma Linolenic Acid (GLA) 2-3%
Poly-unsaturated	Alpha Linolenic Acid 21-25%

Hemp Seed Oil Sample Recipes

These Recipes make 100ml.

Cuticle Cure Oil

60ml Hemp Seed Oil
15ml Sesame Oil
10ml Apricot Kernel Oil
8ml Jojoba Oil
5ml/g Vitamin E Oil (undiluted)
1ml (25 drops) Myrrh Essential Oil
1ml (25 drops) Lemon Essential Oil

Nail Nourisher for brittle nails

45ml Hemp Seed Oil
45ml Sesame Oil
10ml/g Vitamin E Oil (undiluted)
5 drops Rosemary Antioxidant (CO_2 Extract)

Anti-Wrinkle Face Oil for dry, mature Skin

40ml Hemp Seed Oil
20ml Rosehip Oil
20ml Macadamia Nut Oil
18ml/g Vitamin E Oil (undiluted)
2ml/g Echium CO_2 Extract
5 drops Rosemary Antioxidant (CO_2 Extract)

Anti-Wrinkle Face Oil for oily or large-pored skin

58ml Hemp Seed Oil
30ml Rosehip Oil
10ml/g Vitamin E Oil (undiluted)
2ml/g Arctic Cranberry Seed Oil CO_2 Extract
5 drops Rosemary Antioxidant (CO_2 Extract)

Rejuvenating Oil for oily skin

60ml Hemp Seed Oil

25ml Rosehip Oil

5ml Borage Oil

10ml/g Vitamin E Oil (undiluted)

5 drops Rosemary Antioxidant (CO_2 Extract)

Hair Treatment Oil for damaged hair

50ml Hemp Seed Oil

30ml Jojoba Oil

15ml Coconut Butter (melt in bain-marie and add to rest of the blend)

5ml/g Vitamin E Oil (undiluted)

Percentages of Hemp Seed Oil to use in products

Product	Product details	How much Oil you can use in the product	Average use
Skin Rejuvenation/ Anti-Aging products	Face Oils for oily skin	up to 60%	
	Body Oils for oily skin	up to 30%	
	Face Oils and Serums for dry/mature skin	up to 50%	
	Body Oils for dry/mature skin	up to 20%	
	Face Creams for dry/mature skin	up to 15%	8-10%
	Massage Oils for dry/mature skin	up to 20%	
Acne, Eczema and Psoriasis Treatment products	Treatment Creams	up to 12%	8-10%
	Treatment Oils	up to 40%	
Everyday Creams	For all skin types	up to 15%	5-6%
Hair Treatment products	Hair Oil Packs	up to 60%	
Nail Care products	Oil Blends for cuticle care	up to 70%	

Table 21: Percentages of Hemp Seed Oil to use in products

Jojoba Oil

© Jim Andre

Jojoba

INCI name: Simmondsia chinensis

Description

(Pronounced ho-ho-ba.) From an evergreen desert bush which can live up to 100 years old and grows to around three metres high. The cold pressed oil has a clear golden-yellow colour with an odourless or slightly fatty smell. This is not really oil but a liquid wax, which feels dry on the skin. I will refer to it as jojoba oil. The oil is extracted through pressing and the seed contains 50% oil. For skin care, it softens, protects and helps the skin to hold its moisture. Also good as a hair oil and it adds protection to hand creams. It can be used for all skin types and is very good for whole body massage.

The SAP value for jojoba oil is 69-70g.

Absorption Note

Middle.

Natural Vitamin Content

0.05%, or 5mg per 100ml of jojoba oil of naturally occurring vitamin E: alpha-, delta- and gamma tocopherol.

Origin

Used in Mexico, California and Arizona by native American Indians. It is now additionally grown in Argentina, Peru, Israel and Australia.

Shelf Life

Keeps for 4-5 years.

Freezing Point

5°C (+41°F).

Further information

- See page 4 for more information about 'Occlusives'.
- See page 27 for more information about mineral oils and their effect on the skin.

Uses of Jojoba Oil

- Ideal for skin and hair care as jojoba oil is easily absorbed by the skin and has a velvety feeling.
- It softens and protects the skin and improves suppleness.

- Tolerated by most skin types and conditions.
- It has antibacterial and antifungal properties.
- Jojoba is very good for whole body massage. It has a half dry, smooth and non-sticky feeling on the skin. It offers very good lubrication and is absorbed by the skin slowly, which means it is excellent massage oil. It is a long oil. One drop goes a long way so it is very good for long strokes in whole body massage.
- For whole body massage, it provides enough friction reduction (glide) without sacrificing control, although you can add sweet almond, liquid fractionated coconut oil or grape seed oil to give your blend extra spreadability.
- Never use jojoba oil on its own for massage as it does not contain enough (only around 0.5%) of the very nourishing omega 6 and 3 essential fatty acids. Blend it with smaller quantities of thistle, hemp seed or rosehip oil, all of which contain high quantities of essential fatty acids (omega 6 and 3).
- Excellent for face massage oils because of its 'non-stickiness'.
- When used as a massage medium, it acts as an emulsifier with the skin's natural sebum and gently unclogs the pores and lifts grime and imbedded impurities.
- It softens, protects and helps the skin to hold its moisture.
- Its excellent protective qualities make it ideal for hair care products. Furthermore, jojoba oil is not too oily, which makes it easy to wash out of the hair.
- In hair oils and packs for different types of hair and problems, such as dandruff and seborrhoea; dry and damaged hair; to add shine and volume. 100% jojoba oil can be rubbed into hair tips.
- In hair cream treatments for hair loss and for structurally damaged or brittle hair.
- In shampoos, liquid soaps and shower gels. If making an Aromantic recipe for dry hair for one of these, use up to 5% jojoba oil instead of omega in the recipe as the fat restoring agent. Use the same method as you would for adding omega fat restoring agent. **NB** The shampoo will be creamy due to the mix of water and oil.
- Jojoba is excellent to use in lip balms, protective hand and face creams, protective face oils and protective hand foot ointments for farmers, gardeners and in outdoor conditions where the skin is exposed to wind, sun and water as the high content of protective waxes in jojoba oil stops transepidermal water loss. We call this type of moisturiser an 'occlusive' and jojoba is the best vegetable oil-based occlusive.
- As jojoba oil controls transpiration water loss (water and moisture loss through skin) and helps to control flaking and dryness of the skin, it therefore also helps to fight wrinkles.
- Human skin contains layers of waxes, which help to protect the skin and retain moisture. Vaseline® and paraffin can also do this, but jojoba oil does not clog the pores as they do. The high quantity of waxes contained in jojoba oil make it more a liquid wax than a vegetable oil. These waxes are often extracted from the oil to produce jojoba peeling grains or beads for gentle peeling and exfoliating products. Mix the jojoba

peeling grains with castor oil and add to peeling creams and lotions.

- In body lotions. Jojoba oil works well in body lotions because it is a classic long oil and therefore spreads easily over a larger skin surface when applying it to the whole body.

- In baby products it is used to protect sensitive skin and to treat nappy rash.

- In oil-based perfumes. For those who prefer to use non-alcohol based perfumes. Add 20-30% essential oils to jojoba or rice bran oil. Just a note of caution: the aroma of oil-based perfumes can easily be too heavy so be careful not to use too high a percentage of base note essential oils in the perfume. A good percentage guideline for using essential oils in perfumes is: base notes: 30%; middle notes: 20%; and top notes: 50%. Oil-based perfumes don't need to mature for the same length of time as alcohol-based perfumes, but the oil-based perfume is usually more mature after 2-3 weeks of making it.

- Excellent as a base extracting oil to make macerated herbal oils as jojoba oil does not go rancid and keeps for a long time. It blends well with sunflower or olive oil for this purpose.

- 100% jojoba oil can be used as make-up remover.

- It has also been used to treat eczema and psoriasis with good results.

- This oil is special in its chemical make-up. It is very stable for up to 5 years and does not oxidise easily. It is difficult for it to go rancid even when stored or heated for a long time. This stability is due to the fact that it contains only 0.2% polyunsaturated fatty acids (omega 3), and it is these acids that normally cause an oil to go rancid quickly.

- Jojoba is a must in acne treatment products because it is considered that jojoba oil "tricks" the skin into stopping the over-production of sebum through somehow mimicking sebum and also assisting in the breakdown of sebum in plugged-up pores. Sebum and jojoba oil mix readily without "sealing off" the skin pores. In short, a person could say that jojoba oil helps to balance the sebum in all skin types, helping to moisturise dry skin in some people or balancing the over-abundance of oil in others.

- It contains myristic acid, which has anti-inflammatory actions. Since it is similar in composition to the skin's own oils, it is quickly absorbed and is excellent for dry and mature skins, as well as inflamed skin.

- Jojoba oil can be used for cooking as it can be heated to 180°C/356°F but can also be used as a salad dressing.

Fatty Acid (Maximum) Content of Jojoba Oil

Please note, as the percentages below are for the maximum amount of fatty acid content found in jojoba oil, they may add up to more than 100%.

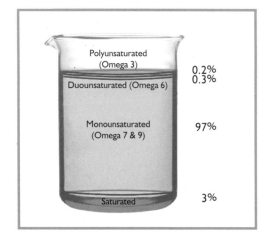

Breakdown of Fatty Acid content of Jojoba Oil	
Saturated	Palmitic Acid <3%
Mono-unsaturated	Oleic Acid 5-15%
	Palmitoleic Acid <1%
	Erucic Acid 10-20%
	Gadoleic Acid 66-88%
Duo-unsaturated	Linoleic Acid 0.3%
Poly-unsaturated	Alpha Linolenic Acid 0.2%

Jojoba Oil Sample Recipes

These Recipes make 100ml.

Swedish Massage Oil

40ml Jojoba Oil
20ml Sweet Almond Oil
15ml Thistle Oil
24ml Coconut Oil, Liquid Fractionated
1ml/g Vitamin E Oil (undiluted)

Eczema Treatment Oil

25ml Jojoba Oil
63ml Rosehip Oil
10ml/g Vitamin E Oil (undiluted)
2ml/g Vitamin A Palmitate
5 drops Rosemary Antioxidant (CO_2 Extract)

Acne Treatment Oil Recipe 1

For everyday use.
20ml Jojoba Oil
49ml Rosehip Oil
20ml Borage Oil
10ml Vitamin E Oil (undiluted)
1ml/g Vitamin A Palmitate
5 drops Rosemary Antioxidant (CO_2 Extract)

Acne Treatment Oil Recipe 2

For everyday use.
20ml Jojoba Oil
20ml Rosehip Oil
23ml Borage Oil
10ml Comfrey Oil
10ml Calendula Oil
15ml/g Vitamin E Oil (undiluted)
2ml/g Vitamin A Palmitate
5 drops Rosemary Antioxidant (CO_2 Extract)

Sports Massage Oil Recipe 1

50ml Jojoba Oil
20ml Coconut Oil, Liquid Fractionated
5ml Thistle Oil
5ml Borage Oil
20ml/g Vitamin E Oil (undiluted)
5 drops Rosemary Antioxidant (CO_2 Extract)

Sports Massage Oil Recipe 2

25ml Jojoba Oil
35ml Coconut Oil, Liquid Fractionated
5ml Thistle Oil
35ml/g Vitamin E Oil (undiluted)
10 drops Rosemary Antioxidant (CO_2 Extract)

Sports Massage Oil Recipe 3

40ml Jojoba Oil
25ml Coconut Oil, Liquid Fractionated
5ml Thistle Oil
5ml Borage Oil
25ml/g Vitamin E Oil (undiluted)
5 drops Rosemary Antioxidant (CO_2 Extract)

Hair Treatment Oil for damaged hair and scalp

30ml Jojoba Oil
25ml Sunflower Oil
10ml Calendula Oil
10ml Moringa Oil
19ml Sesame Oil
5ml/g Vitamin E Oil (undiluted)
1ml/g Vitamin A Palmitate
5 drops Rosemary Antioxidant (CO_2 Extract)

Nappy Rash Treatment Oil

35ml Jojoba Oil
20ml Calendula Oil
20ml Thistle Oil
10ml Apricot Kernel Oil
5ml St. John's Wort Oil
9ml/g Vitamin E Oil (undiluted)
1ml/g Vitamin A Palmitate
5 drops Rosemary Antioxidant (CO_2 Extract)

Percentages of Jojoba Oil to use in products

Product	Product details	How much Oil you can use in the product	Average use
Massage products for all skin types	Whole Body Massage Oil Blends	up to 50%	
	Facial Massage Oils	up to 35%	
Skin Protection products	Protective Face Oils	up to 50%	25-35% for non-extreme weather
	Protective Hand Creams	up to 15%	12-15%
Lip Balms	Can be used instead of Oils in Recipe but will alter existing Recipes due to Jojoba's high wax content.		
Face Creams	For all skin types	up to 10%	5-7%
Body Lotions	Note about using Jojoba Oil in Body Lotions: As you usually only use a maximum of 15% of Fats/Oils in a Lotion and Emulsifiers will be 7% of that, Jojoba Oil on average another 4-5%, leaving 3% for adding another Fat/Oil to the Body Lotion.	up to 6%	4-5%

/contd

contd/

Product	Product details	How much Oil you can use in the product	Average use
Hair Treatment products	Dandruff and seborrhoea Hair Treatment Oils	up to 95%	
	Hair Treatment Oils for shine and volume	up to 75%	
	Dry and damaged Hair Treatment Oils. Apply to hair tips.	100%	
	Hair Cream Treatments for structurally damaged/brittle hair	up to 15%	9-11%
	Hair Loss Cream Treatments	up to 15%	8-10%
Eczema & Psoriasis products	Treatment Creams	up to 8%	3-4%
	Treatment Oils	up to 20%	
Acne Treatment products	Everyday Acne Cure/ Treatment Oils	up to 20%	
	Treatment Creams	up to 10%	5-7%
Skin Protection products	Hand and Foot Ointments	up to 50%	
Baby products	Everyday use Creams	up to 15%	12-15%
	Skin Protection Oil Blends	up to 40%	
	Nappy Rash Oil Treatment Blends	up to 30%	
Oil-based Perfumes		Add 20-30% Essential Oils to Jojoba Oil e.g. to make 100ml of Perfume, add 20-30% Essential Oils to 80-70% Jojoba Oil.	
Macerated Herbal Oils	Use the Jojoba as a base/ extraction Oil for macerating herbs.	up to 100%	
Make-up products	Make-up Remover Oil	up to 100%	
Cleansing and Peeling products	Use Jojoba Peeling Grains instead of the Jojoba Oil	Use 5-6% Jojoba Peeling Grains together with 5-6% Castor Oil in Peeling Creams and Lotions.	

Table 22: Percentages of Jojoba Oil to use in products

Kiwi Seed Oil

Kiwi

INCI name: Actinidia chinensis or deliciosa

Description

A lot of people simply enjoy eating the kiwi fruit without realising its nutritional benefits. It is a rich source of phytonutrients, vitamins A and C, potassium and magnesium, as well as dietary fibre and the enzyme group, actinidin. In addition, we now know that the seeds of the kiwi fruit are a rich source of essential fatty acids.

Less than 3% of the total weight of the kiwi fruit is made up of the seeds, which yield approximately 35% of their weight as oil when processed. The seeds are very small and delicate; separation from the pulp takes place via a special process developed in New Zealand. The seeds are then stabilised and subsequently cold pressed to yield the oil. The temperature needs to be kept less than 30°C during the cold pressing process. Once this is done, a good producer will stabilise the oil with natural antioxidants as well as storing or bottling it in nitrogen-flushed containers. This is very important due to the high amount of omega 3 fatty acids present in kiwi seed oil and would otherwise go rancid in a few weeks after production.

The oil has a light yellow colour. The crude oil is often dark brown in colour and has a characteristic odour. In order to make the oil suitable for use in the cosmetic industry, it is further refined to yield a lighter coloured, almost odourless product. It is a dry, smooth and soft oil very high in alpha linolenic acid (up to 65%) and so is excellent in formulations treating sensitive or dry skin and hair.

The SAP value of kiwi seed oil 196g.

Absorption Note

Top.

Natural Vitamin Content

The fruit itself is rich in vitamins C and A. I haven't seen any data for the vitamin content of the oil. Of course it contains up to 80% of vitamin F (Omega 3 and 6 fatty acids). The oil is said to be rich in vitamin E oil, but again I have no data to back this up.

Origin

Native to southern China and is also called Chinese gooseberry but has been grown in New Zealand for 60 years.

Shelf Life

Due to the high content of polyunsaturated fatty acids you should never buy kiwi seed oil that does not have added vitamin E oil or other natural antioxidants, otherwise it will go rancid within 6 months. Adding 0.5% undiluted vitamin E oil, or an equivalent antioxidant, will increase the shelf life to 2 years.

Freezing Point

Unknown to me but an educated guess would be that it is comparable with that of flaxseed oil, i.e. -20 to -25°C (+41 to +50°F).

Further information

- See page 7 for More information on essential fatty acids (vitamin F).
- See page 15 for 'Rebalancing certain skin types with certain vegetable oils'.
- See page 29 for 'Tips for buying borage, camelina, evening primrose, hemp seed, kiwi seed and rosehip oils.

Uses of Kiwi Seed Oil

- Kiwi seed oil is excellent for treating sensitive and oily and large-pored skin, as well as helping to treat all kinds of skin infections, such as acne, eczema, psoriasis, pimples and boils. It is also useful in the repair of damaged skin tissue, varicose veins and skin over-exposed to sunlight, and reducing or healing fine lines around the eyes, wrinkles and scars.

- Its consistency is dry to very dry and kiwi seed oil is considered to be one of the best anti-wrinkle oils available today. It soothes fine wrinkles, especially around the eyes and mouth. It gives elasticity to the skin and helps against skin aging. Add it to anti-wrinkle and skin rejuvenation face serums, skin oils and creams. It is ideal for including in highly nutritious face serums.

- In face oils. The oil has a short surface time on the skin, being rapidly absorbed by the skin and not leaving any fatty residue, which makes it excellent face oil. It can also be used undiluted (100%).

- In eye creams due to kiwi seed oil's dryness and softness.

- In formulations to help reduce skin redness.

- If you want to make a lighter cream or lotion, kiwi seed oil is ideal.

- In after sun products. Kiwi seed oil is very healing for skin damaged by, or over-exposed to, ultraviolet radiation from the sun or x-ray radiation. Always add vitamin A and E oils to these products.

- Because it is very high in omega 3 alpha linolenic acid (up to 65%), you can take it internally instead of marine oils or flaxseed oil (up to 42% omega 3) in salad dressings or as a food supplement (1-2 teaspoons a day). The body naturally converts between 2% and 10% of the ALA into eicosapentanoeic acid (EPA) and docosahexaenoic acid (DHA). It is because of this, that it has been described a true vegetarian alternative to marine oils.

- The high alpha linolenic acid content of kiwi seed oil helps to maintain moisture in the skin and hair and so makes it a useful ingredient in the treatment of dry skin and hair problems. Include it in any formulation for healing dry, scaled or damaged skin or dry hair.

- The body also uses the essential fatty acids contained in kiwi seed oil to help maintain the proper flexibility of cells' membranes and to restore the proper cholesterol/triglyceride ratio. This keeps our cell membranes soft and pliable and that helps the cells to function optimally in terms of taking in nutrients and expelling waste.
- It's an excellent emollient with extremely good skin penetration. This and its non-oiliness makes it a good choice for adding to body and face lotions.
- Hydrating and moisturising.
- It's a very dry, thin, soft and smooth oil. It is truly remarkable that an oil can be as dry as kiwi seed oil and yet so soft and smooth. These properties make it ideal for use on sensitive skin.
- Spreads well on the skin, so good for adding to massage oil blends in small quantities, mainly as a rich source of omega 3 fatty acid.
- Excellent for treating large pores due to kiwi seed oil's high content of omega 6 and 3 essential fatty acids, which help to reduce the size of pores.
- In baby products. Blend with fattier oils such as rice bran, avocado and apricot kernel.
- In oil blends for healing bedsores.
- Kiwi seed oil reduces the fattiness of other vegetable oils in blends. By adding kiwi seed oil, you reduce the

overall melting point of fats in your skin, allowing the body to process them easier.

- Kiwi seed oil has a fatty acid content similar to that found in marine fauna such as sharks and the sperm whale and is now used as a replacement for sperm whale oil in cosmetics.

Fatty Acid (Maximum) Content of Kiwi Seed Oil

Please note, as the percentages in this illustration are for the maximum amount of fatty acid content found in kiwi seed oil, they may add up to more than 100%.

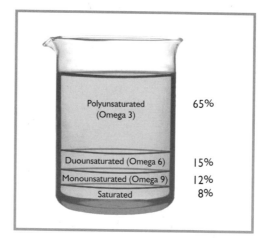

Polyunsaturated (Omega 3)	65%
Duounsaturated (Omega 6)	15%
Monounsaturated (Omega 9)	12%
Saturated	8%

Breakdown of Fatty Acid content of Kiwi Seed Oil	
Saturated	Palmitic Acid 5%
	Stearic Acid 3%
Mono-unsaturated	Oleic Acid 11.6%
	Vaccenic Acid <0.3%
Duo-unsaturated	Linoleic Acid 15%
Poly-unsaturated	Alpha Linolenic Acid 60-65%

Kiwi Seed Oil Sample Recipes

These Recipes make 100ml.

Face Serum for all skin types

70ml Kiwi Seed Oil
20ml/g Vitamin E Oil (undiluted)
8ml Rosehip Oil
2ml/g Vitamin A Palmitate
5 drops Rosemary Antioxidant (CO_2 Extract)

Face Lift Serum for dry skin

60ml Kiwi Seed Oil
10ml Evening Primrose Oil
10ml Pumpkin Seed Oil
20ml Vitamin E Oil (undiluted)
5 drops Rosemary Antioxidant (CO_2 Extract)

Face Serum for oily/large-pored skin

80ml Kiwi Seed Oil
5ml Evening Primrose Oil
15ml Vitamin E Oil (undiluted)
5 drops Rosemary Antioxidant (CO_2 Extract)

Face/Anti-Wrinkle Oil for mature skin

60ml Kiwi Seed Oil
10ml Rosehip Oil
10ml Macadamia Nut Oil
18ml/g Vitamin E Oil (undiluted)
1ml/g Vitamin A Palmitate
1ml/g Echium Seed CO_2 Extract
5 drops Rosemary Antioxidant (CO_2 Extract)

Face/Anti-Wrinkle Oil for sensitive and large-pored skin

85ml Kiwi Seed Oil
15ml/g Vitamin E Oil (undiluted)
5 drops Rosemary Antioxidant (CO_2 Extract)

Face/Anti-Wrinkle Oil for oily skin

60ml Kiwi Seed Oil
10ml Evening Primrose Oil
10ml Rosehip Oil
10ml/g Vitamin E Oil (undiluted)
8ml Jojoba Oil
2ml/g Vitamin A Palmitate
5 drops Rosemary Antioxidant (CO_2 Extract)

Face/Anti-Wrinkle Oil for dry skin

85ml Kiwi Seed Oil
13ml/g Vitamin E Oil (undiluted)
2ml/g Vitamin A Palmitate
5 drops Rosemary Antioxidant (CO_2 Extract)

Kiwi Seed Daily Acne Treatment Oil

Apply every evening.
56.5ml Kiwi Seed Oil
10ml Rosehip Oil
10ml Borage Oil
10ml Jojoba Oil
10ml/g Vitamin E Oil (undiluted)
2ml/g Vitamin A Palmitate
1.5ml Aromantic's Anti-Acne Active Formula
5 drops Rosemary Antioxidant (CO_2 Extract)

Scar Tissue Treatment Oil

For general use. Apply up to twice a day.

25ml Kiwi Seed Oil

15ml Rosehip Oil

10ml Borage Oil

50ml/g Vitamin E Oil (undiluted)

10 drops Rosemary Antioxidant (CO_2 Extract)

Kiwi Baby Oil

For general use. It's softening, calming and healing.

30ml Kiwi Seed Oil

20ml Rosehip Oil

36ml Apricot Kernel Oil

10ml Calendula Oil

3ml/g Vitamin E Oil (undiluted)

1ml/g Chamomile CO_2 Extract

Percentages of Kiwi Seed Oil to use in products

Product	Product details	How much Oil you can use in the product	Average use
Skin Rejuvenation/ Anti-Wrinkle/Anti-Aging products	Anti-Wrinkle Creams	up to 10%	6-8%
	Anti-Wrinkle Face Oils/Serums	up to 80%	
	Rejuvenating Body Oils	up to 35%	
Creams for sensitive skin	Everyday Creams for sensitive & dry skin	up to 10%	4-6%
	Everyday Creams for sensitive & oily skin	up to 7%	5-6%
Acne Treatment products	Treatment Creams	up to 12%	6-8%
	Treatment Oils	up to 65%	
Eczema and Psoriasis Treatment products	Treatment Creams	up to 10%	5-6%
	Treatment Oils	up to 60%	
Sun Care and Protection products	After-Sun Oils	up to 50%	
Baby products	Everyday Baby Creams	up to 10%	5-7%.
	Nappy Rash Treatment Oils	Up to 50% - blend with fattier Oils.	
Hair Treatment products	Everyday use Hair Treatment Oils	up to 20%	
	Hair/Scalp Cure Treatment Oils	up to 70%	

/contd

contd/

Product	Product details	How much Oil you can use in the product	Average use
X-ray radiation/Sun Eczema Treatment products	Treatment Oils	up to 45%	
Skin Tissue Treatment products	Scar Tissue Oil Blends	up to 50%	25%
	Oil Treatment Blends for treating damaged skin tissue	30-50%	
Varicose Veins Treatment products	Treatment Oils	up to 40%	
	Treatment Gels	up to 50%	
Circulation Treatment products	Treatment Oils	up to 70%	

Table 23: Percentages of Kiwi Seed Oil to use in products

Macadamia Nut Oil

Macadamia Nut
INCI name: Macadamia tetraphylla

Description

This vegetable oil is pressed from the nuts of the *Macadamia tetraphylla* tree, which originated in Australia and was discovered by John Macadam in the 1930's. It now grows all over South America and in Kenya and the South Pacific Islands. The powdered macadamia nuts, which contain about 75% oil, are cold pressed without heating (i.e. under 30°C). The resulting oil is clear, light yellow to golden-yellow. It does not smell very strong but has a pleasant nutty taste and is a very fatty oil which is soft, smooth and nice to use. Despite its fattiness, which varies from fatty to very fatty, the skin readily, but slowly, absorbs it. It is especially good to use for mature and dry skin and skin which has difficulty retaining its moisture.

The SAP value for macadamia nut oil is 139g.

Absorption Note
Base.

Natural Vitamin Content
Unknown to me.

Origin
Australia, South America, Kenya, Pacific Islands.

Shelf Life
Keeps for 2-5 years.

Freezing Point
+5°C (+41°F).

Contraindications/warnings
Check for nut allergies with client.

Uses of Macadamia Nut Oil

- It is the most important oil for mature skin.
- Macadamia nut oil feels fatty, thick, soft and sticky on the skin and can take up to one hour to be absorbed. This is known as a long 'surface time', providing good lubrication which makes it

excellent for whole body massage oils. Once absorbed, it leaves skin soft and smooth.

- The fatty surface of macadamia nut oil protects against weather and wind, helps to keep moisture in the skin and to treat dry areas of skin and hands and feet, so use in protective creams, ointments, balms, lotions and face oils. Always blend with jojoba oil and drier oils such as thistle, hemp seed and rosehip for this purpose.

- In anti-aging and anti-wrinkle oil blends, creams and lotions. Macadamia nut oil is the best choice for people with mature or dry skin due to the high content of palmitic acid, which is vital to reduce the skin's aging process. Always blend with drier oils such as thistle, rosehip and hemp seed oils.

- In creams for everyday use for mature and dry skin.

- In sun care oils and creams.

- For around the eye care creams and oils.

- As a base extraction oil for making macerated herbal oils because macadamia nut oil keeps well. Blend with the drier sunflower oil for this purpose.

- Tolerated by most skin types but not recommended for oily or acne skin or skin with large pores.

- The oil can be used safely around the eyes and for skin with circulation problems.

- Excellent for adding to sun care products as it has a natural sun protection factor (SPF) of 4 and it counteracts the skin aging process when sunbathing.

Fatty Acid (Maximum) Content of Macadamia Nut Oil

Please note, as the percentages in this illustration are for the maximum amount of fatty acid content found in macadamia nut oil, they may add up to more than 100%.

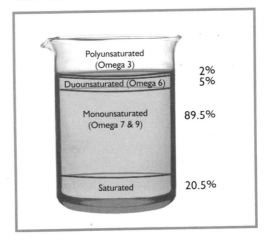

Polyunsaturated (Omega 3)	2%
Duounsaturated (Omega 6)	5%
Monounsaturated (Omega 7 & 9)	89.5%
Saturated	20.5%

Breakdown of Fatty Acid content of Macadamia Nut Oil	
Saturated	Palmitic Acid 7-9.5%
	Stearic Acid 2-6%
	Arachidic Acid 1.5-3%
	Lauric Acid <1%
	Myristic Acid <1%
Mono-unsaturated	Oleic Acid 52-67%
	Palmitoleic Acid 20%
	Eicosenoic Acid 1.5-2.5%
Duo-unsaturated	Linoleic Acid ≤5%
Poly-unsaturated	Alpha Linolenic Acid ≤2%

The Fatty Acid Content gives Macadamia Nut Oil special qualities

- It keeps well (2-5 years).
- It should not be used on oily or large-

pored skin as it can clog pores and enlarge them due to its high content of saturated fatty acids (up to 20%).

- It contains only up to 2% of essential fatty acids, so it is not very nourishing. You can therefore blend it with vegetable oils rich in essential fatty acids, such as thistle oil (safflower oil) or borage oil for more nourishment.

- Macadamia nut oil is unlike other vegetable oils as it contains a high level of palmitoleic acid (up to 20%), a fatty acid that is also found in mink oil (oil from dead minks). Mink oil is still used in a number of skin care products, but macadamia nut oil can be used instead.

- Palmitoleic acid also occurs naturally in our skin, where its job is to maintain moisture levels. The level of palmitoleic acid is reduced with age, which results in drier skin. Macadamia nut oil is therefore a good ingredient to have in products for dry and older and mature skin.

- The skin absorbs macadamia nut oil easily. It can be used in face oils, massage oils, creams, lotions, etc.

Macadamia Nut Oil Sample Recipes

These Recipes make 100ml.

Massage Oil for mature and sensitive skin

30ml Macadamia Nut Oil
30ml Apricot Kernel Oil
20ml Thistle Oil
10ml Jojoba Oil
5ml Borage Oil
5ml/g Vitamin E Oil (undiluted)
5 drops Rosemary Antioxidant (CO_2 Extract)

Body and Massage Oil for dry or mature skin Recipe 1

40ml Macadamia Nut Oil
45ml Thistle Oil
5ml Castor Oil
10ml/g Vitamin E Oil (undiluted)
5 drops Rosemary Antioxidant (CO_2 Extract)

Body and Massage Oil for dry or mature skin Recipe 2

40ml Macadamia Nut Oil
25ml Thistle Oil
20ml Borage or Evening Primrose Oil
10ml Apricot or Peach Kernel Oil
5ml/g Vitamin E Oil (undiluted)
5 drops Rosemary Antioxidant (CO_2 Extract)

Anti-Wrinkle/Skin Rejuvenation Face Oil for mature or sensitive skin

30ml Macadamia Nut Oil
33ml Rosehip Oil
20ml Evening Primrose Oil
15ml/g Vitamin E Oil (undiluted)
2ml/g Echium CO_2 Extract
5 drops Rosemary Antioxidant (CO_2 Extract)

Eye Care Oil for dry or mature skin

For use around the eyes.
10ml Macadamia Nut Oil
77.5ml Rosehip Oil
10ml/g Vitamin E Oil (undiluted)
1ml Sea Buckthorn CO_2 Extract
0.5ml/g Chamomile CO_2 Extract
5 drops Rosemary Antioxidant (CO_2 Extract)

Anti-wrinkle Face Oil for mature skin

50ml Macadamia Nut Oil
30ml Thistle Oil
5ml Evening Primrose Oil
15ml/g Vitamin E Oil (undiluted)
5 drops Rosemary Antioxidant (CO_2 Extract)

Face Oil for Smokers with dry or mature skin

15ml Macadamia Nut Oil
70ml Borage or Evening Primrose Oil
5ml Thistle Oil
10ml/g Vitamin E Oil (undiluted)
5 drops Rosemary Antioxidant (CO_2 Extract)

Percentages of Macadamia Nut Oil to use in products

Product	Product details	How much Oil you can use in the product	Average use
Skin Rejuvenation/ Anti-Aging products for mature/dry skin	Creams and Lotions	up to 15%	10-12%
	Skin Rejuvenation Oil Blends	Up to 50% - always blend with drier Oils.	
	Face Oils for mature and dry skin	up to 40%	
Creams NB! Always mix with drier Oils!	Everyday Creams for dry and mature skin	up to 15%	8-12%
Skin Protection products	Skin Protection/Hand Creams	Up to 15% - combine with Jojoba Oil for skin protection.	8-10%
	Protective Ointments and Balms	up to 30%	
Around-the-Eye Care products	Eye Care Creams	up to 6%	3-4%
	Eye Care Oils	up to 15%	
Sun Protection and Care products	Sun Creams for mature/dry skin	up to 15%	10-12%
	Sun Oil Blends	up to 30%	
Massage products for mature/dry skin	Whole Body Massage Oil Blends	up to 50%	
Macerated Herbal Oils	Use the Macadamia Nut as a base/extraction Oil together with Sunflower Oil for macerating herbs.	up to 50%	

Table 24: Percentages of Macadamia Nut Oil to use in products

Moringa Oil

high concentration of behenic acid) that can be used in cooking, cosmetics, and for lubrication. The refined oil is clear and odourless; cold pressed oil ranges from odourless to slightly nutty aroma and flavour. The seed cake remaining after oil extraction may be used as a fertiliser or as a flocculent to purify water. The oil is also considered a very high quality illuminant as it burns clearly and cleanly.

The SAP value for moringa oil is 164g.

Absorption Note

Base.

Natural Vitamin Content

I am not aware of any documented information on the natural vitamin content of moringa oil at the time of writing this book. Moringa oil is often referred to as being vitamin-rich by those companies selling it, but actually the only documented nutritional profiles I could find were for moringa shoots, flowers, leaves and fruit. These food products seem to have many excellent benefits for good human nutrition and for medicinal use. Here is an example of the nutritional value of the leaves, which are low in fats and carbohydrates and rich in minerals, iron and vitamin B: they contain gram for gram 7 times the vitamin C found in oranges, 4 times the

Moringa

INCI name: Moringa oleifera

Description

Synonyms: drumstick tree, horseradish tree (because of the taste of the leaves). *Moringa oleifera*, commonly referred to simply as moringa, is the most widely cultivated variety of the genus *Moringa*. The tree itself is rather slender with drooping branches that grow to approximately 10m in height. Considered one of the world's most useful trees, as almost every part of the moringa tree can be used for culinary purposes, or has some other beneficial property. According to the Indian Ayurvedic system of health, the moringa tree can prevent over 300 diseases.

The moringa seeds yield 38-40% edible oil (often called ben oil, because of its calcium in milk, 4 times the vitamin A in carrots, 2 times the protein in milk, and 3 times the potassium in bananas.

Origin

The moringa tree grows mainly in semi-arid tropical and subtropical areas. While it grows best in dry sandy soil, it tolerates poor soil, including coastal areas. It is a fast-growing, drought-resistant tree. A native of the sub-Himalayan regions of northwest India, *Moringa oleifera* is now indigenous to many countries in Africa, Arabia, South East Asia, the Pacific and Caribbean Islands and South America.

Shelf Life

Keeps for 4-5 years.

Freezing Point

+20°C (+68°F).

Uses of Moringa Oil

- For skin care, moringa oil has excellent antioxidant properties and is high in oleic acid, both of which are considered to be the factors behind its remarkable oxidative stability and therefore long shelf life. It also has nourishing, cleansing and emollient properties. It is a light oil and as it is a long oil that offers excellent lubrication, it spreads easily on the skin. This makes it an excellent massage or aromatherapy oil or ingredient in creams, lotions, peeling and cleansing scrubs, balms, and hair care products.

- It gives hair a shine when used in hair oils, an excellent gloss to the lips when added to lip glosses, and makes skin shiny and luminescent when applied to the skin in face or skin oils.

- Commercially, the flowers, leaves and fruit pods are mainly used. The vegetable oil is also used for culinary purposes as cooking oil or a salad dressing and for cosmetics.

- For the purpose of skin care, moringa is a very good emollient and so is an excellent choice for mature and dry skin products such as creams, lotions, ointments and oil blends, etc. See page 4 for more information about emollients.

- Its fatty acid content is similar to both macadamia nut oil and olive oil. The quantities of omega 9 monounsaturated fatty acids gives it good lubricating properties and makes it particularly suitable for whole body massage.

- As it is a relatively new oil for us in the west, we need to learn what people living in the countries of its origin are using the oil for. The bark, sap, roots, leaves, seeds, oil and flowers are used as food, cosmetics and in traditional medicine in several countries.

- Villagers in Oman use the oil to treat stomach disorders and also as a perfume oil and hair oil.

- In the Philippines, people use it as an extraction oil for macerating the moringa flowers. The resulting macerated oil is then applied topically for the relief and treatment of arthritic and rheumatic pains and gouty joints, and so it would indicate that the oil has anti-inflammatory properties.

- The flowers are also cooked and relished as a delicacy in West Bengal and Bangladesh, especially during early spring and are usually cooked with green peas and potato.

- Moringa leaves are eaten as a highly nutritious leaf vegetable, particularly in the Philippines, India and Africa.

- In addition to being used fresh as a substitute for spinach, its leaves are commonly dried and crushed into a powder, and used in soups and sauces. In Tamil Nadu, a southern state of India, it is used in this way in Siddha medicine.

- The fruit of the tree is quite popular as a vegetable in Asia and Africa. The fruit is a long, thin pod, resembling a drumstick. These immature green pods are probably the most valued and widely used part of the tree. They are commonly consumed in India, and are generally prepared in a similar fashion to green beans and have a slight asparagus taste.

- The seeds are sometimes removed from more mature pods and roasted or eaten in the same way as we eat peas.

- In Jamaica, the sap is used for a blue dye.

- The leaves are used as a pesticide and the wood as fuelwood.

- Its high oleic acid content makes moringa oil an excellent choice for frying or cooking at high temperatures.

Fatty Acid (Maximum) Content of Moringa Oil

Please note, as the percentages in this illustration are for the maximum amount of fatty acid content found in moringa oil, they may add up to more than 100%.

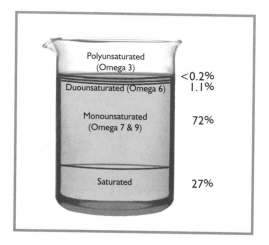

Polyunsaturated (Omega 3)	<0.2%
Duounsaturated (Omega 6)	1.1%
Monounsaturated (Omega 7 & 9)	72%
Saturated	27%

Breakdown of Fatty Acid content of Moringa Oil	
Saturated	Palmitic Acid 7.8%
	Stearic Acid 7.6%
	Arachidic Acid 4%
	Lignoceric Acid 1.3%
	Myristic Acid 0.1%
	Behenic Acid 6.2%
Mono-unsaturated	Oleic Acid 67.9-68.6%
	Palmitoleic Acid 1.5%
	Eicosenoic Acid 1.4%
Duo-unsaturated	Linoleic Acid 1.1%
Poly-unsaturated	Linolenic Acid 0.2%

Moringa Oil Sample Recipes

These Recipes make 100ml.

Moringa Hair Treatment Oil for dry hair or dry, irritated scalp

40ml Moringa Oil

40ml Thistle Oil

15ml Calendula Oil

5ml/g Vitamin E Oil (undiluted)

5 drops Rosemary Antioxidant (CO_2 Extract)

Glossy Lips

A healing oil blend that also gives the lips a glossy shine.

40ml Moringa Oil
30ml Castor Oil
11ml Jojoba Oil
5ml/g Vitamin E Oil (undiluted)
2ml/g Bisabolol
1ml/g Vitamin A Palmitate
5 drops Rosemary Antioxidant (CO_2 Extract)
10-15 drops of Essential Oils of your choice

Method for making and using Glossy Lips

1) Measure the ingredients in a small beaker.
2) Blend together well.
3) Pour into a small roll-on bottle/s.
4) Apply to lips once to several times a day.

Moringa Hair Oil

Gives the hair a lovely shine.

50ml Moringa Oil
28ml Thistle Oil
10ml Castor Oil
10ml/g Vitamin E Oil (undiluted)
2ml/g Bisabolol
5 drops Rosemary Antioxidant (CO_2 Extract)

Moringa Hair Treatment Oil for dry hair or dry, irritated scalp

40ml Moringa Oil
40ml Thistle Oil
15ml Calendula Oil
5ml/g Vitamin E Oil (undiluted)
5 drops Rosemary Antioxidant (CO_2 Extract)

Luminous Face Oil for dry, mature and sensitive skin

Nourish your skin and give your face a luminous glow at the same time!

30ml Moringa Oil
30ml Rosehip Oil
25ml Evening Primrose Oil
10ml Castor Oil
4ml/g Vitamin E Oil (undiluted)
1ml/g Bisabolol

Moringa Anti-Wrinkle Oil Blend

Reduce and prevent fine lines and give your face a luminous glow at the same time!

30ml Moringa Oil
25ml Rosehip Oil
23ml Borage Oil
5ml Castor Oil
15ml/g Vitamin E Oil (undiluted)
2ml/g Bisabolol
5 drops Rosemary Antioxidant (CO_2 Extract)

Shiny Moringa Massage Oil for dry, mature and sensitive skin

A nourishing massage oil with excellent lubricating properties that gives your skin a luminous glow at the same time!

50ml Moringa Oil
16ml Macadamia Nut Oil
20ml Thistle Oil
10ml Castor Oil
3ml/g Vitamin E Oil (undiluted)
1ml/g Bisabolol

Percentages of Moringa Oil to use in products

Product	Product details	How much Oil you can use in the product	Average use
Massage Oil Blends	For dry/mature skin	up to 50%	
Moisturising products that also give your skin a luminous glow	Creams and Lotions for dry, mature skin	up to 15%	8-10%
	Face Oil for dry, mature skin	up to 30%	
	Anti-Wrinkle Face Oils	up to 20%	10-15%
Macerated Herbal Oil	For making Macerated Herbal Oils – use with Sunflower Oil as a bsae extraction oil.	up to 50%	
Hair Care products	Hair Oils and Packs	up to 50%	
Pain-relief products	Arthritis, rheumatism and gout Treatment Oils	up to 50%	
Perfumes	Oil-based Perfumes	up to 50%	

Table 25: Percentages of Moringa Oil to use in products

Mullein Oil

Mullein

INCI name: Verbascum thapsus and usually the INCI name for the oil that the Mullein is macerated in.

Description

Synonyms: Common mullein, great mullein.

This is a macerated oil. Macerated mullein oil ranges from yellow to green. A natural wrinkle-fighter, mullein contains vitamins, minerals, tannins and useful levels of elastin, so can be combined with pumpkin seed oil for a lifting effect. The oil that the mullein is macerated in is decisive in how the oil feels on the skin.

For the SAP value, refer to the oil that the mullein has been macerated in.

Natural Vitamin Content

Mullein contains calcium, iron, potassium, sulphur, vitamins A, B and D (but the quantities are unknown to me). Also refer to the vegetable oil that the mullein is macerated in for further vitamin content.

Origin

Mullein is a widely distributed plant, being found all over Europe and in temperate Asia as far as the Himalayas, and in North America. In Britain, Ireland and the Channel Islands Mullein is found on hedgebanks, waste ground and by the side of the road.

Shelf Life

Refer to the oil that the mullein has been macerated in.

Freezing Point

Refer to the oil that the mullein has been macerated in

Further information

- See page 29 for how to make an oil compress.

Uses of Mullein Oil

- Mullein oil contains tannin so it is effective in barrier creams for the skin. It also contains calcium, iron, potassium, sulphur, and vitamins A, B and D.

- As it is a mild painkiller, add to oil blends for sports or other muscle or tendon injuries. Adding comfrey oil to these blends is also recommended.
- In medicated lip balms that help to treat the oral herpes simplex virus i.e. cold sores (add up to 5% tea tree and 1% lavender essential oils).
- It calms inflammations where nerves have been irritated (combine with St. John's wort oil).
- It is extensively used in the cosmetic industry and can be added to acne, eczema and psoriasis creams.
- It is good for oily/combination skin types. See page 16 for more information about combination skin.
- Because of its useful levels of elastin, it would blend well with pumpkin seed oil where you need a lifting effect.
- It rehydrates and moisturises. Can be added, along with jojoba and olive oil, to hair oil packs or products for treating the scalp.
- Mullein is a natural wrinkle fighter and skin-regenerating oil.
- In a cotton wool compress applied to the ear to relieve earache. Slightly warming the mullein oil makes the compress even more soothing and comforting.
- Mullein oil contains glycyrrhizin compounds with bactericide and potential anti-tumoural action. Different extracts have varying levels of efficiency against bacteria and topical application of the oil can be used for warts, boils, carbuncles, haemorrhoids, and chilblains.

Fatty Acid (Maximum) Content of Mullein Oil

Refer to the fatty acid chart and breakdown table of the oil that the mullein has been macerated in.

Mullein Oil Sample Recipes

These Recipes make 100ml.

Hair Oil

10ml Mullein Oil

40ml Jojoba Oil

40ml Sesame Oil

10ml/g Vitamin E Oil (undiluted)

5 drops Rosemary Antioxidant (CO_2 Extract)

Cold Sore Treatment Oil

Good for treating herpes simplex (cold sores).

15ml Mullein Oil

45ml Rosehip Oil

10ml Calendula Oil

5ml St. John's Wort Oil

10ml Calendula Oil

10ml/g Vitamin E Oil (undiluted)

1.5ml/g Vitamin A Palmitate

3ml Tea Tree Essential Oil

0.5ml (12 drops) Lavender Essential Oil

5 drops Rosemary Antioxidant (CO_2 Extract)

Method

1) Mix together in a glass beaker or jar.

2) Pour the blend into a small roll-on bottle and apply 2-3 times a day.

Sore Muscle Oil

For use before and after sports.
20ml Mullein Oil
37ml Thistle Oil
15ml Comfrey Oil
15ml Calendula Oil
10ml/g Vitamin E Oil (undiluted)
2ml/g Chamomile CO_2 Extract
1ml/g Sea Buckthorn CO_2 Extract
5 drops Rosemary Antioxidant (CO_2 Extract)

Face-Lifting Oil for all skin types

Apply to your face in the evenings.
10ml Mullein Oil
64ml Rosehip Oil
8ml Pumpkin Seed Oil
15ml/g Vitamin E Oil (undiluted)
2ml/g Echium Seed CO_2 Extract
1ml/g Sea Buckthorn CO_2 Extract
5 drops Rosemary Antioxidant (CO_2 Extract)

Percentages of Macerated Mullein Oil to use in products

Product	Product details	How much Oil you can use in the product	Average use
Skin Protection products	Barrier Hand Creams	Up to 15% - also add Jojoba Oil to the Blend.	8-10%
Earache Treatment products	Earache Cotton Wool Compress	Use 100% Oil on the cotton wool.	
Sports Injuries Treatment products	Treatment Oil Blends	up to 25%	
Hair Treatment products	Hair Oil Packs and Hair Treatment Oils	up to 10%	
Medicated Lip products	Medicated Lip Balms	Replace the Vegetable Oil/s in the Recipe with Mullein Oil.	
	Medicated Lip Oils	up to 60%	
Eczema and Psoriasis Treatment products	Treatment Creams	up to 10%	5-6%
	Treatment Oils	up to 15%	
Skin Regeneration and Skin Lifting products	Lifting/Regeneration Creams	up to 8%	4-5%
	Face Oils	up to 15%	
	Body Oils	up to 20%	

Table 26: Percentages of Mullein Macerated Oil to use in products

Mustard Seed Oil

Mustard

INCI name: Brassica nigra

Description

The mustard plant is a small annual plant, which grows up to a height of one metre and has soft yellowish-green leaves. The fruit is a pod, about 2.5cm long and contains the seeds, which are famously very small, less than 1mm in diameter. Mustard seed oil has a pleasant, nutty flavour and is not hot or 'mustardy'. It is cold pressed from the whole seed and it is then filtered through cotton and paper and bottled. The resulting oil retains the characteristic colour, aroma and taste of the oil of the parent seed during processing, and the hot elements (or the pungent taste) do not enter the oil during pressing. At 5%, mustard seed oil has the lowest saturated fat content of the edible oils and has a high percentage of omega 3 fatty acids.

The SAP value for mustard seed oil is 124g.

Absorption Note

Middle.

Natural Vitamin and Mineral Content

Mustard seed oil contains a high quantity of selenium and is rich in betacarotene, which stimulates the production of vitamin A. It also contains tryptophan (an essential amino acid), phosphorous, manganese, magnesium, iron, calcium, vitamin B3 (niacin), zinc. There is said to be vitamin E in mustard seed oil, but the quantity is unknown to me.

Origin

Black mustard is a native of Eurasia. It has been in cultivation in Europe for a long time. *Brassica nigra* was the first species to provide table mustard for use as a condiment. Romans, Greeks and Indians have used it since ancient times. The plant is cultivated as a field crop in most temperate countries. It is currently widely used in northern India.

Shelf Life

Keeps for 3 years.

Freezing Point

Unknown to me.

Restrictions on the use of Mustard Seed Oil

Quoting Wikipedia: "due to its high content of erucic acid, which is considered noxious, mustard seed oil is not considered suitable for human consumption in the United States, Canada and the European Union, although mustard seed oil with a low content of erucic acid is available. In India, mustard seed oil is generally heated almost to smoking before it is used for cooking; this may be an attempt to reduce the content of noxious substances, and does reduce the strong smell and taste. In India the restrictions on mustard seed oil are viewed as an attempt by foreign multinational corporations to replace mustard seed oil with canola oil, a variety of rapeseed with a low erucic acid content. But for northern Indians, mustard seed oil is not just a cooking medium but it is very much intricately interwoven with their culture. They have been using it for ages and dispute that there is enough evidence for the toxicity of erucic acid, instead maintaining that mustard seed oil is beneficial to human health because of its low content of saturated fats, ideal ratio of omega 6 and omega 3 fatty acids, content of antioxidants and vitamin E, as well as the fact that it is cold pressed (extracted at 45-50°C)."

Further information

- See page 29 for how to make an oil compress.

Uses of Mustard Seed Oil

- In Indian head massage oil blends.
- In massage oil blends for whole body massage.

- Mustard is a rubefacient, which causes reddening and warming of the skin. This makes it an excellent ingredient in oil blends that treat muscular aches and pains and rheumatism. Being an excellent source of selenium also makes mustard seed oil useful for decreasing some of the symptoms of rheumatoid arthritis.

- Mustard seed oil boiled with henna leaves is used for encouraging healthy hair growth. Boil about 25g of mustard seed oil, adding a few grams of henna leaves at a time, until you have added about 60g of henna leaves and they have been heated in the mustard seed oil. Filter the oil through a cloth and store it in a bottle. Regular head massage with this oil will improve hair growth.

- At 5%, mustard seed oil has the lowest saturated fat content of all of the vegetable oils. In addition, the oil naturally has what is considered by some the ideal ratio of 2:1 of omega 6 and omega 3 essential fatty acids. They are essential because our body can't produce them and we must have them in an adequate supply to keep our bodies healthy. Deficiency can result in a gradual deterioration of the body's cells and tissues.

- Mustard seed oil, along with sunflower and sesame seed oils, is heated and used for Indian head massage. The oils are heated as it makes it easier to work with as well as the skin absorbing it faster. Also, mustard seed oil contains large amounts of the mineral selenium, which is very nourishing for hair.

- Due to restrictions on its use in certain countries and regions, we recommend mustard seed oil for external use only.

Fatty Acid (Maximum) Content of Mustard Seed Oil

Please note, as the percentages in the following illustration are for the maximum amount of fatty acid content found in mustard seed oil, they may add up to more than 100%.

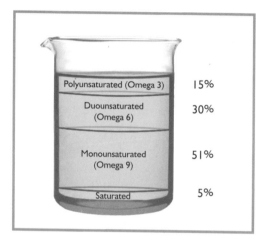

Polyunsaturated (Omega 3)	15%
Duounsaturated (Omega 6)	30%
Monounsaturated (Omega 9)	51%
Saturated	5%

Breakdown of Fatty Acid content of Mustard Seed Oil	
Saturated	Palmitic Acid 3%
	Stearic Acid 2%
Mono-unsaturated	Oleic Acid 30%
	Erucic Acid 19-21%
Duo-unsaturated	Linoleic Acid 28-30%
Poly-unsaturated	Alpha Linolenic Acid 13-15%

Mustard Seed Oil Sample Recipes

These Recipes make 100ml.

Indian Skin and Massage Oil

50ml Mustard Seed Oil
30ml Sesame Oil
16g Coconut Butter
3ml/g Vitamin E Oil (undiluted)
Essential Oils (optional): 8 drops ylang ylang, 8 drops sandalwood, 4 drops vetivert.

Method

1) First, melt the coconut butter in a bain-marie.
2) Then, mix all of the vegetable oils together with the coconut butter.
3) Add the vitamin E oil.
4) Add the essential oils (optional).
5) Bottle and label

Nourishing Indian Head Massage Oil

60ml Mustard Seed Oil
20ml Sesame Oil
14ml Sunflower Oil
5ml/g Vitamin E Oil (undiluted)
5 drops Rosemary Antioxidant (CO_2 Extract)
15–20 drops Essential Oils (optional)

Mustard Seed Muscle Oil

For soothing muscular aches and pains.
50ml Mustard Seed Oil
40ml Thistle Oil
5ml Castor Oil
5ml/g Vitamin E Oil (undiluted)
5 drops Rosemary Antioxidant (CO_2 Extract)

Percentages of Mustard Seed Oil to use in products

Product	Product details	How much Oil you can use in the product	Average use
Massage products	Indian Head Massage Oil Blends	up to 60%	
	Whole Body Massage Oil Blends	up to 50%	
Pain relief products	Oil Blends for treating muscular aches and pains	up to 50%	
Hair Oil	See Recipe under 'Uses'	up to 30%	

Table 27: Percentages of Mustard Seed Oil to use in products

Neem Oil

Neem

INCI name: Melia azadiracta

Description

Neem oil is pressed from the seed kernel of the neem tree, which contains about 50% oil. The tree is evergreen and can live for up to 200 years and up to a height of 20-25 metres. The oil is a thick, light to dark brown in colour, bitter and fatty oil, which has a rather strong odour that has been likened to a combination of peanut and garlic. The strong odour and colour makes it difficult to use in skin care products but it is a very useful oil with powerful antibacterial and antifungal properties. You can use it in small areas of the body or in small quantities in blends. The use of neem has a 4,000-year tradition in Ayurvedic medicine in India, where the tree is considered holy. Neem oil contains steroids (campesterol, betasitosterol, and stigmasterol) and a variety of triterpenoids, of which azadirachtin is the best known and studied. It has a high azadirachtin content that varies from 300 parts per million to 2000 parts per million, depending on the quality of the seeds crushed. It is this active ingredient, azadirachtin, which works as an insecticide, fungicide and antibacterial agent.

The SAP value for neem oil is 134g.

Absorption Note

Base.

Natural Vitamin Content

Unknown to me.

Origin

The tree is native to India and Burma but can now be found in Africa and southeast Asia as well.

Shelf Life

Keeps for 1.5-2 years.

Freezing Point

+15 to +20°C (+59 to +68°F).

Uses of Neem Oil

- Neem oil has powerful antibacterial and antifungal properties, which makes it excellent for a number of different uses.

- As an antiseptic skin oil to help treat eczema and psoriasis.
- In hair packs to get rid of lice, or to treat dandruff, etc. Jojoba oil is an excellent oil to mix with neem oil when making hair oils.
- It is a good choice for treating wounds and haemorrhoids.
- It has traditionally been used as an insect repellent.
- In antifungal nail oil blends.
- In healing nail oil blends. It helps to stop the nails from splitting.
- In antiseptic foot care products.
- The strong odour and colour makes it difficult to use in skin care products but it is a very useful oil with powerful antibacterial and antifungal properties. You can use it in small areas of the body or in small quantities in blends.
- I recommend that you buy cold pressed neem oil, but there is also a lot of neem oil on the market that has been extracted with the use of heat or chemicals.

How Neem Oil is used in India and Bangladesh

- Neem oil has an extensive history of human use in India and surrounding regions for a variety of therapeutic purposes. Neem oil is not generally used in these regions for cooking purposes but, in India and Bangladesh, it is used for preparing cosmetics such as soap, hair products, body hygiene creams, hand creams, etc and in Ayurvedic, Unani and other traditional medicines it is used in the treatment of a wide range of afflictions, varying from fever to leprosy.

- Ancient Ayurvedic writings show that the oil was used most frequently for treating skin diseases, inflammations and fevers, and more recently for treating rheumatic disorders, as well as for its insect repellent and insecticidal properties.
- Formulations including neem oil also find wide usage as biopesticides for organic farming, as it repels a wide variety of pests. Neem oil is non-toxic to mammals and birds as well as many beneficial insects such as honeybees and ladybugs. Neem oil also controls black spot, powdery mildew, anthracnose and rust.

Tips for using Neem Oil

When using neem oil in a recipe, always add some essential oils with strong base notes, such myrrh and benzoin to cover up the smell.

Fatty Acid (Maximum) Content of Neem Oil

Please note, as the percentages in this illustration are for the maximum amount of fatty acid content found in neem oil, they may add up to more than 100%.

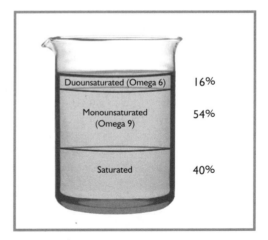

Duounsaturated (Omega 6)	16%
Monounsaturated (Omega 9)	54%
Saturated	40%

Breakdown of Fatty Acid content of Neem Oil	
Saturated	Palmitic Acid 13-18%
	Stearic Acid 15-20%
	Arachidic Acid 2%
Mono-unsaturated	Oleic Acid 50-54%
Duo-unsaturated	Linoleic Acid 6-16%

Neem Oil Sample Recipes

The Recipes make 100ml.

Antiseptic/Antifungal Foot Ointment

Keeps for 2 years.

Stage 1

20ml Neem Oil
13g Beeswax
61ml Thistle Oil

Stage 2

4ml/g Vitamin E Oil (undiluted)
2ml (25 drops) of antiseptic Essential Oils, such as fragonia, tea tree, sandalwood and lavender.

Method

1) Melt the Stage 1 ingredients in a bain-marie (double boiler).
2) Remove from heat and place the heatproof bowl (or top part of the double boiler) in a cold water basin. Stir the contents with a spoon or a whisk.
3) When the mixture has the consistency of thick soup, stir in the pre-measured ingredients from Stage 2.
4) Quickly pour into jars

Anti-Dandruff Hair Oil

10ml Neem Oil
40ml Walnut Oil
35ml Jojoba Oil
10ml Castor Oil
3ml/g Vitamin E Oil (undiluted)
2ml (50 drops) Essential Oils, e.g. Tea Tree, Lavender and Sandalwood.

How to use

1) Shake mixture before using.
2) In the evening, massage enough of the mixture into hair and scalp in order to cover the whole scalp and all of the hair.
3) Leave on for 1 hour.
4) Wash out by applying a shampoo to the scalp and hair before rinsing with water. Then wash the hair with running lukewarm-to-hot water

Antifungal/Antibacterial Nail Oil

Apply at least once a day to your nails.
10ml Neem Oil
40ml Sesame Oil
35ml Thistle Oil
10ml/g Vitamin E Oil (undiluted)
1ml Sea Buckthorn CO_2 Extract
1ml Carrot CO_2 Extract
1ml/g Vitamin A Palmitate
2ml (50 drops) Essential Oils: fragonia (20 drops), tea tree (20 drops), lavender (5 drops), myrrh (5 drops)
5 drops Rosemary Antioxidant (CO_2 Extract)

Percentages of Neem Oil to use in products

Product	Product details	How much Oil you can use in the product	Average use
Insect Repellents	Thin Lotion	Up to 20% - you need to add Citronella Essential Oil to the Recipe.	8-10%
	Insect Repellent Oil Blends	Up to 20% - you need to add Citronella Essential Oil to the Recipe.	10-15%
Nail Care products	Antifungal and Healing Nail Oil Blends	up to 20%	5-10%
Hair products	Hair Oils and Packs	Up to 15% combined with 85% Jojoba Oil and Essential Oils.	
Foot Treatment products	Antiseptic Oil Blends	up to 30%	5-10%
	Foot Creams	up to 5%	

Table 28: Percentages of Neem Oil to use in products

Olive Oil

Olive
INCI name: Olea europa

Description

The olive tree is small, with grey-green leaves and has been harvested for its olives and the oil, which can be pressed from the olives, for at least 9000 years. The olive tree grows very slowly, only bearing fruit typically after fifteen years, but after that it can live and bear fruit for hundreds of years. The tree flowers in late spring, bearing white blossoms. The fruit develops over the summer and autumn months and is harvested in November and December. The unripe olives are green and blacken when ripening. Green olives are picked while unripe, which makes them denser and more bitter than brown or black olives, which stay on the tree until fully ripened. Raw olives must be cured before they are eaten. The nearly ripened black olives are picked for oil production and contain 50-55% oil. The oil is found in the fruit of the olive flesh, not the kernel.

The nearly ripe olives are pressed as soon as possible; storing them after harvesting creates free fatty acids, which reduces the quality of the oil. Virgin olive oils are obtained only from the olive using solely mechanical or other physical means in conditions, particularly thermal conditions, which do not alter the oil in any way. These oils have not undergone any treatment other than washing, decanting, centrifuging and filtering. It excludes oils obtained by the use of solvents or re-esterification methods, and those mixed with oils from other sources. Extra virgin olive oil is the oil extracted when olives are first pressed. Officially, the acidity must be no more than 0.8% of acidity per 100 grams of the extra virgin oil. The lower the acidity of the olive oil, the higher the quality, and the more distinctive the flavours and aromas. Virgin olive oil has a free acidity of not more than 2% or 2 grams per 100 grams. Ordinary virgin olive oil has a free acidity of not more than 3.3% or 3.3 grams per 100 grams. Ordinary olive oil may still be fine for frying or where flavour is not wanted or needed. Cold pressed refers to oil which has been pressed at below 30°C, which is considered to produce the best flavour. After pressing the oil it is centrifuged and filtered. Refined olive oil can be defined as oil that has been refined with the use of charcoal and other chemical and physical filters (no solvents were used in its extraction).

Extra virgin and virgin olive oil have a distinctly green olive taste that comes from the chlorophyll. The aroma is slightly fruity.

Traditionally and to this day olive oil is used in many skin, hair and body care products as well as for culinary purposes in salad dressings, on bread, with cheese, vegetables, meat and fish dishes.

The SAP value for olive oil is 134-140g.

Olive Oil is an important part of the Mediterranean diet

The Mediterranean diet is a modern nutritional model inspired by the traditional dietary patterns of some of the countries of the Mediterranean basin, particularly Greece and Southern Italy. The Mediterranean diet is not a specific diet plan or diet program but a collection of eating habits that are traditionally followed by the people of the Mediterranean region. Common to the diets of these regions are a high consumption of fruit and vegetables, bread, wheat and other cereals, olive oil, fish, and red wine. The diet is often cited as beneficial for being low in saturated fat and high in monounsaturated fat and dietary fibre.

It is based on what from the point of view of mainstream nutrition is considered a paradox: that although the people living in Mediterranean countries tend to consume relatively high amounts of fat, they have far lower rates of cardiovascular disease than in countries like the United States, where similar levels of fat consumption are found.

A way to resolve this paradox is to take into account the large amount of olive oil used in the Mediterranean diet. Unlike the high amount of animal fats typical to the American diet, olive oil lowers cholesterol levels in the blood. It is also known to lower blood sugar levels and blood pressure. In addition, the consumption of red wine is considered a possible factor, as it contains flavonoids with powerful antioxidant properties.

According to scientists, people who eat a typical Mediterranean diet are healthier and have fewer heart problems than northern Europeans and Americans and others who eat similarly but dietary factors may be only part of the reason for the health benefits enjoyed by these cultures. Genetics, lifestyle, and environment may also be involved. The traditional Mediterranean diet is very popular in many parts of the world now but is amended to suit food source and availability. For this reason it is often called the new, or modified, Mediterranean diet. As we already know, we can benefit from any oil's properties by using it on the skin in various cosmetic products.

It is classic cooking oil, with a high smoke point of over +210°C/+410°F.

Absorption Note

Base.

Natural Vitamin Content

Approximately 0.001% (1mg per 100ml of olive oil) naturally occurring vitamin E (delta tocopherol); 0.14mg per 100g of vitamin A; 1mcg per 100g betacarotene (the more yellow the oil, the betacarotene it contains); 0.1mcg per 100g of vitamin K.

Other important constituents of Olive Oil

Chlorophyll: Up to 0.001%, or 1mg per 100ml of olive oil of chlorophyll (higher content if less ripe olives are used). It helps to heal the skin.

Phenols: Extra virgin olive oil is rich in polyphenols, which are known to be anti-inflammatory, antioxidant and anticoagulant.

Oleocanthal: Is a non-steroidal anti-inflammatory and antioxidant. It's a non-selective inhibitor of cyclooxygenase (COX) that causes relief of inflammation and pain.

Squalane: Is derived from olive oil and is absorbed quickly by the skin. It is well proven that squalane increases the spreadability of vegetable oils and fats on the skin. The substance squalene is also found in the livers of sharks that are found in deep ocean waters and studies have shown that it keeps the oils in the liver in a liquid state down to a temperature of -38°C. Olive-oil derived squalane helps to regulate sebum and very closely resembles human sebum. For use as an emollient, squalane is a traditional, natural alternative to using silicone emollients, which is an often-used chemical in products for its non-fatty skin-softening properties.

Origin

It is native to the Mediterranean but also grows in California, Mexico and Australia. Experts locate the origin of olive tree culture on the edge of the Mediterranean Sea, on the coasts of the Lebanon and Palestine, which were dominated by Phoenicians between 6,000-5,000 BCE.

Shelf Life

Due to its high oleic acid content it keeps well, up to 3 years.

Freezing Point

0 to +5°C (+32 to +41°F). Fractions of the solid fatty acid solidify at the higher temperature of +10°C (+50°F).

Further information

- See page 4 for more information on 'Occlusives'.

Uses of Olive Oil

- Due to its fattiness, it's very good for dry, mature and sensitive skin products.
- Don't use it on oily or large-pored skin because it is too oily for oily skin types and will easily enlarge the pores.
- However, the olive oil's fattiness protects the skin against the elements and stops transepidermal water loss, helping to keep moisture in the skin. This type of moisturiser is called an occlusive; it protects your skin with an oily layer. For this purpose it works well in ointments and oilier creams.
- It is a classic oil for dry, chapped skin on elbows, knees, hands and feet.
- Used in hand creams, it offers nourishing, softening and excellent protection from weather and water.
- In foot creams it offers the necessary level of fattiness and protection that feet need.
- Olive oil strengthens the capillary walls and so is good to use on skin that bruises easily. Combine with drier oils as well as arnica oil for treating sprains and bruises in oil blends and compresses.

- Olive oil is an excellent addition to whole body massage oils as it is both soft and long and therefore offers excellent lubrication and a soft, smooth feeling on the skin. The problem can be that it has quite an overpowering smell, so remember to blend it with more neutral smelling, drier oils such as thistle (refined), jojoba or grape seed oils as examples.

- As already mentioned, olive oil has nourishing, softening and protecting properties. It is also anti-inflammatory and so very valuable to use in oil blends that treat skin irritations, insect bites, sun-damaged skin, eczema, psoriasis and itchiness.

- It is also heating, so good to use for the treatment of rheumatic pains.

- Excellent for hair products treating dry hair and dry, damaged scalp or an irritated and sensitive scalp.

- Very good for using on the legs for the prevention of leg ulcers and poor circulation. Blend it with thistle or grape seed oil and apply to the feet and legs for the relief of poor blood circulation, coldness, cramps, swollenness, ulcers, aches and pains, and broken nails.

- After coconut fat or oil, olive oil is the most used oil/fat in the making of soaps. It produces a hypoallergenic soap that is excellent for people with sensitive skin.

Fatty Acid (Maximum) Content of Olive Oil

Please note, as the percentages in the following illustration chart are for the maximum amount of fatty acid content found in olive oil, they may add up to more than 100%.

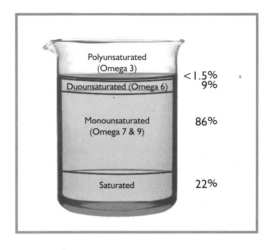

Breakdown of Fatty Acid content of Olive Oil	
Saturated	Palmitic Acid 6-15%
	Stearic Acid 1-5%
	Arachidic Acid <1%
	Myristic Acid ≤1%
	Behenic Acid <0.3%
Mono-unsaturated	Oleic Acid 55-85%
	Palmitoleic Acid <1%
Duo-unsaturated	Linoleic Acid 5-9%
Poly-unsaturated	Alpha Linolenic Acid ≤1.5%

Olive Oil Sample Recipes

These Recipes make 100ml.

Body and Massage Oil for dry, mature, sensitive skin Recipe 1
30ml Olive Oil
30ml Apricot Kernel Oil
20ml Thistle Oil
10ml Jojoba Oil
5ml Borage Oil
5ml/g Vitamin E Oil (undiluted)
5 drops Rosemary Antioxidant (CO_2 Extract)

Body and Massage Oil for dry, mature, sensitive skin Recipe 2

40ml Olive Oil

35ml Thistle Oil

10ml Sunflower Oil

5ml Castor Oil

10ml/g Vitamin E Oil (undiluted)

5 drops Rosemary Antioxidant (CO_2 Extract)

Body and Massage Oil for dry, mature, sensitive skin Recipe 3

35ml Olive Oil

20ml Thistle Oil

20ml Evening Primrose Oil

10ml Sunflower Oil

10ml Peach Kernel Oil

5ml/g Vitamin E Oil (undiluted)

4 drops Rosemary Antioxidant (CO_2 Extract)

Hair Oil for structurally damaged hair

25ml Olive Oil

25ml Rice Bran Oil

20ml Jojoba Oil

18ml Thistle Oil

5ml Calendula Oil

5ml/g Vitamin E Oil (undiluted)

1ml/g Vitamin A Palmitate

1ml (25 drops) Lavender Essential Oil

10 drops Sandalwood Essential Oil

4 drops Rosemary Antioxidant (CO_2 Extract)

Anti-inflammatory Treatment Oil

30ml Olive Oil

20ml St. John's Wort Oil

20ml Rosehip Oil

18ml Evening Primrose Oil

7ml/g Vitamin E Oil (undiluted)

1ml/g Vitamin A Palmitate

2ml/g Sea Buckthorn CO_2 Extract

2ml/g Chamomile CO_2 Extract

4 drops Rosemary Antioxidant (CO_2 Extract)

Protective Baby Oil

Apply 1-2 times a day.

25ml Olive Oil

15ml Sesame Oil

15ml Peach Kernel Oil

15ml Rosehip Oil

15ml Jojoba Oil

10ml Peach Kernel Oil

5ml/g Vitamin E Oil (undiluted)

4 drops Rosemary Antioxidant (CO_2 Extract)

Soothing Baby Oil

Apply 1-2 times a day.

25ml Olive Oil

20ml Sesame Oil

20ml Apricot Kernel Oil

10g Shea Butter (melt in a bain-marie before adding to the blend)

10ml Rosehip Oil

10ml Jojoba Oil

5ml/g Vitamin E Oil (undiluted)

4 drops Rosemary Antioxidant (CO_2 Extract)

Swedish Massage Oil

33ml Olive Oil
20ml Sweet Almond Oil
15g Coconut Butter (melt in a bain-marie before adding to the blend)
15ml Jojoba Oil
15ml Apricot Kernel Oil
2ml/g Vitamin E Oil (undiluted)

Simple Swedish Massage Oil

30ml Olive Oil
20ml Sweet Almond Oil
20ml Jojoba Oil
20ml Thistle Oil
8ml Apricot Kernel
2ml/g Vitamin E Oil (undiluted)

Percentages of Olive Oil to use in products

Product	Product details	How much Oil you can use in the product	Average use
Products for dry, mature, sensitive skin types	Whole Body Massage Oils	up to 50%	
	Face Oils	up to 10%	
	Body Oils	up to 30%	
	Cream for mature skin	up to 12%	5-7%
	Cream for dry skin	up to 15%	5-7%
Skin Rejuvenation/ Anti-Aging products for dry, mature, sensitive skin types	Face Creams	up to 10%	5-7%
	Body Lotions	up to 8%	4-5%
Skin Cleansing products	Make-up Remover Oil Blends	Up to 50% - you could combine it with Castor Oil, which is very good Cleansing Oil.	
Body Oils	Body Oils for dry/mature skin	up to 20%	
Massage products	Massage Oils for dry/ mature skin	up to 20%	
Skin Protection products	Protective Ointments and Balms	Up to 60%	
	Hand Creams	Up to 15% - also add Jojoba Oil for added protection. Maximum total for both Oils is 20%.	8-10%

/contd

contd/

Eczema, Psoriasis and Sun damaged Skin Treatment products	Treatment Creams	up to 10%	5-7%
Hair Care products	Oil Hair Packs and Hair Treatments	up to 30%	
Sun Protection and Care products	Creams	up to 16%	10-12%
	Oils	up to 50%	
Lip Care products	Lip Balms	Up to 40% as the main Vegetable Oil in the Recipe for its softening and gliding effects.	35-40%
Baby products	Baby Oils	up to 30%	
	Baby Creams	up to 15%	8-10%
	Nappy Rash Creams	up to 15%	10-12%
Foot Care products	Foot Creams	up to 15%	10-12%
Anti-inflammatory products	Anti-inflammatory Oil Blends	up to 40%	
Anti-itching products	Anti-itching/irritation Skin Oil	up to 40%	

Table 29: Percentages of Olive Oil to use in products

Peach Kernel Oil

Peach

INCI name: Prunus persica

Description

A semi-fatty oil that has the same properties as apricot kernel oil. The oil is clear, light yellow with a slight smell and mild taste. The peach kernel provides around 32-45% oil, which is stable and semi-fatty. Its qualities are that it spreads well and is easily absorbed by the skin. It is absorbed quite slowly (20-50 minutes) and is therefore excellent for use in whole body massage oil blends. It is a mild oil, which is tolerated by most people, and is especially good for sensitive, inflamed, dry or mature skin. It enhances skin elasticity and has a soft and smooth quality on the skin. Refined peach kernel oil can be used for high temperature cooking.

The SAP value for peach kernel oil is 135g.

Absorption Note

Middle.

Natural Vitamin Content

0.001%, or 1mg per 100ml of peach kernel oil of vitamin E.

Origin

The scientific name *Persica* derives from an early European belief that peaches were native to Persia (now Iran). However, the modern consensus is that it originates from China and was introduced to Persia and the Mediterranean region along the Silk Road around 2000BCE. Nowadays it is grown mostly around the Mediterranean.

Shelf Life

2-3 years.

Freezing Point

-15°C (+5°F).

Uses of Peach Kernel Oil

- It is a classic skin oil for sensitive skin.
- All the *Prunus* oils, i.e. almond, peach and apricot kernel oils have very

similar properties and effects on the skin and all leave the skin feeling soft and smooth. Peach and apricot are the most similar.

- I regard peach and apricot kernel oils to be interchangeable for products that treat sensitive skin. They will always form the basis for any product I make for that skin type, with the exception of sensitive skin that is also oily. In that case rosehip oil would form the basis of the recipe.

- In anti-wrinkle/skin rejuvenation products for sensitive skin.

- In massage lotions and oils for sensitive skin. Peach kernel oil is a long oil. A drop goes a long way and so is very good for long strokes in whole body massage.

- In skin cleansers and peelers for sensitive skin.

- In products that treat eczema and itchy skin conditions.

- In acne treatment creams and oils.

- In lip balms, simply replace the vegetable oil/s in the recipe with apricot kernel oil.

- Used as cooking oil in Asia but seldom used for cooking in Europe.

Fatty Acid (Maximum) Content of Peach Kernel Oil

Please note, as the percentages in the following illustration are for the maximum amount of Fatty Acid content found in peach kernel oil, they may add up to more than 100%.

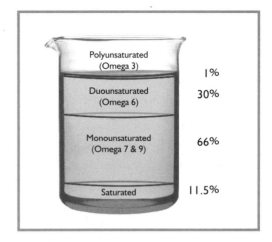

Breakdown of Fatty Acid content of Peach Kernel Oil	
Saturated	Palmitic Acid 5-6%
	Stearic Acid 2-5%
	Arachidic Acid <0.5%
Mono-unsaturated	Oleic Acid 60-65%
	Palmitoleic Acid ≤1%
Duo-unsaturated	Linoleic Acid 25-30%
Poly-unsaturated	Alpha Linolenic Acid ≤1%

Peach Kernel Oil Sample Recipes

These Recipes make 100ml.

Rejuvenating Whole Body Massage Oil for all skin types
40ml Peach Kernel Oil
20ml Thistle Oil
15ml Rosehip Oil
10ml Borage/Evening Primrose Oil
15ml/g Vitamin E Oil (undiluted)
4 drops Rosemary Antioxidant (CO_2 Extract)

Swedish Massage Oil for sensitive, mature, dry skin types

50ml Peach Kernel Oil

15ml Macadamia Nut Oil

12ml Coconut Butter (melt first in a bain-marie and then add to the blend)

10ml Thistle Oil

10ml Rosehip Oil

3ml/g Vitamin E Oil (undiluted)

Face Oil for sensitive skin

30ml Peach Kernel Oil

40ml Borage/Evening Primrose Oil

20ml Rosehip Oil

10ml/g Vitamin E Oil (undiluted)

4 drops Rosemary Antioxidant (CO_2 Extract)

Daily use Baby Oil

60ml Peach Kernel Oil

38ml Rosehip Oil

2ml/g Vitamin E Oil (undiluted)

Healing Baby Oil

Apply when necessary, for e.g. nappy rash, itchiness, red skin, etc.

50ml Peach Kernel Oil

27ml Rosehip Oil

10ml Calendula Oil

5ml Comfrey Oil

5ml/g Vitamin E Oil (undiluted)

1ml/g Vitamin A Palmitate

1ml/g Chamomile CO_2 Extract

1ml/g Sea Buckthorn CO_2 Extract

5 drops Rosemary Antioxidant (CO_2 Extract)

Anti-Wrinkle Face Oil/Serum for sensitive skin

30ml Peach Kernel Oil

25ml Rosehip Oil

25ml Evening Primrose Oil

20ml/g Vitamin E Oil (undiluted)

5 drops Rosemary Antioxidant (CO_2 Extract)

Percentages of Peach Kernel Oil to use in products

Product	Product details	How much Oil you can use in the product	Average use
Creams	Sensitive skin	up to 15%	10-12%
	Mature/dry skin	up to 12%	8-10%
Massage and Body Care products	Whole Body Massage/Skin Oils for sensitive skin	up to 70%	
	Whole Body Massage/Skin Oils for all other skin types	up to 40%	
	Massage Lotions for sensitive skin	Up to 60% - remember to use Emulsifan CB Emulsifier.	40-50%
	Massage Lotions for all other skin types	up to 40%	20-30%

/contd

contd/

Product	Product details	How much Oil you can use in the product	Average use
Acne Treatment products	Treatment Creams	up to 10%	5-6%
	Treatment Oils	up to 30%	15-20%
Eczema and Psoriasis Treatment products	Treatment Creams	up to 15%	6-8%
	Treatment Oils	up to 40%	20-30%
Skin Rejuvenation/ Anti-Wrinkle products for sensitive skin	Creams	up to 12%	10-12%
	Face Oils/Serums	up to 30%	20-25%
	Rejuvenating Body Oils	up to 50%	25-35%
	Eye Creams	up to 10%	6-8%
Cleansing and Peeling products for sensitive skin	Cleansing Oils	up to 70%	
	Cleansing or Peeling Creams	up to 50%	20-30%
Baby products	Everyday use Baby Oil	up to 70%	
	Everyday use Baby Creams	up to 16%	12-14%
Anti-itching products	Anti-itching Skin Oil	up to 60%	
Lip products	Lip Balms	Replace up to 100% of the Vegetable Oil content in the Recipe.	

Table 30: Percentages of Peach Kernel Oil to use in products

Pumpkin Seed Oil

Pumpkin
INCI name: Cucurbita maxima

Description

Pumpkin seed oil is cold pressed from the seeds and has a dark, yellow-orange colour with a powerful taste and smell. It is high in vitamins A, betacarotene, B2, B3, potassium, magnesium and most importantly zinc. It is also high in omega 9, 6 and 3. Because of its high zinc content it is an excellent lifting oil for dry, mature and damaged skin. The oil is well known, and taken internally, for its beneficial effect on prostate problems.

The SAP value for pumpkin seed oil is 133g.

Absorption Note
Middle.

Natural Vitamin Content

Said to contain high quantities of vitamin A, betacarotene, and vitamins B2 and B3 but the exact quantities are unknown to me.

Origin

Cultivated in North America, continental Europe, Australia, India and some other countries, all species of pumpkin plants are native to the western hemisphere. They are being grown more in Europe now due to a revival of the celebration of Halloween.

Shelf Life

Keeps for 1.5-2 years.

Freezing Point
-15°C (+5°F).

Contraindications for Pumpkin Seed Oil

NB Pregnant and lactating women should not use pumpkin seed oil or its products.

Uses of Pumpkin Seed Oil

- In products where a lifting effect is required, so it can be used in facial, abdominal, upper leg, breast and buttock lifting/firming preparations.

- Due to its strong smell, use less oil in facial products.
- Excellent for use in products treating dry, mature skin.
- A popular supplement for prostate health (taken internally).

Fatty Acid (Maximum) Content of Pumpkin Seed Oil

Please note, as the percentages below are for the maximum amount of fatty acid content found in pumpkin seed oil, they may add up to more than 100%.

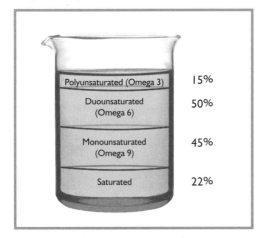

Polyunsaturated (Omega 3)		15%
Duounsaturated (Omega 6)		50%
Monounsaturated (Omega 9)		45%
Saturated		22%

Breakdown of Fatty Acid content of Pumpkin Seed Oil	
Saturated	Palmitic Acid 13-15%
	Stearic Acid 5-7%
Mono-unsaturated	Oleic Acid 35-45%
Duo-unsaturated	Linoleic Acid 35-50%
Poly-unsaturated	Alpha Linolenic Acid 15%

Pumpkin Seed Oil Sample Recipes

Face-lifting Recipes for different skin types. Each Recipe makes 100ml.

Face-lifting Oil/Serum for dry skin

10ml Pumpkin Seed Oil
40ml Rosehip Oil (non-organic)
25ml Thistle Oil
10ml Evening Primrose Oil
15g/ml Vitamin E Oil (undiluted)
5 drops Rosemary Antioxidant (CO_2 Extract)

Face-lifting Oil/Serum for mature skin

10ml Pumpkin Seed Oil
44ml Rosehip Oil (non-organic)
10ml Macadamia Nut Oil
20ml Evening Primrose Oil
15g/ml Vitamin E Oil (undiluted)
1ml/g Sea Buckthorn CO_2 Extract
5 drops Rosemary Antioxidant (CO_2 Extract)

Face-lifting Oil/Serum for sensitive and dry skin

8ml Pumpkin Seed Oil
52ml Rosehip Oil, non-organic
20ml Apricot Kernel Oil
10ml Evening Primrose Oil
10g/ml Vitamin E Oil (undiluted)
5 drops Rosemary Antioxidant (CO_2 Extract)

Face-lifting Oil/Serum for oily skin

5ml Pumpkin Seed Oil
50ml Rosehip Oil, non-organic
30ml Evening Primrose Oil
10ml/g Vitamin E Oil (undiluted)
5ml Mullein Oil
5 drops Rosemary Antioxidant (CO_2 Extract)

Percentages of Pumpkin Seed Oil to use in products

Product	Product details	How much Oil you can use in the product	Average use
Face-lifting products	Lifting Oil Blends/Serums	up to 15%	
	Lifting Creams	up to 8%	4-6%
Bust-firming products	Firming Oil Blends	up to 20%	
	Firming Creams	up to 10%	
Buttock-firming products	Firming Oil Blends	up to 20%	
	Firming Creams	up to 12%	
Skin Rejuvenation/ Anti-Wrinkle products	Anti-Wrinkle Creams for dry, mature Skin	up to 8%	4-5%

Table 31: Percentages of Pumpkin Seed Oil to use in products

Rice Bran Oil

Rice
INCI name: Oryza sativa

Description

A half-fatty to half-dry oil traditionally used in Japan. Known for its mild and softening properties on the skin. A good source of omega 6 essential fatty acid and various antioxidants that have benefits for human health. Rice bran oil is a by-product of the rice milling process and is extracted from rice bran; which, in turn, is extracted from brown rice. A major part of the rice bran contains 12-13% oil and other constituents such as tocotrienol (a vitamin E fraction that is a potent antioxidant, many times more powerful than tocopherol); gamma-oryzanol; betasitosterol; and ferulic acid. The ferulic acid is an antioxidant, which neutralises free radicals that could cause oxidative damage to the cell membranes and the DNA and helps to protect the skin from damage caused to it by ultraviolet light. It contains up to 2% gadoleic acid, which is also found in cod liver oil.

So, to summarise, rice bran oil applied to the skin fosters surface microcirculation and skin metabolism, providing protection against premature aging. It influences oil secretion, absorbs UV rays and helps prevent oxidation and is well known for its considerable nourishing properties and so is often used in anti-aging blends and products.

The SAP value for rice bran oil is 128g.

Absorption Note

Middle.

Natural Vitamin Content

0.04%, or 40mg per 100ml of rice bran oil of vitamin E (naturally-occurring d-alpha tocopherol). Also contains significantly high quantities of naturally occurring tocotrienols, but the exact quantities are unknown to me. (Tocotrienols together with tocopherols comprise the vitamin E family.)

Origin

Traditionally from India, Japan and China. Now also produced by USA, Indonesia and Brazil.

Shelf Life

Keeps for 2-3 years.

Freezing Point

-5 to -10°C (+23 to +14°F).

Uses of Rice Bran Oil

- Rice bran oil is a very versatile oil. It is excellent for dry, sensitive skin and newly created skin such as baby skin but also for mature skin because of the oil's high antioxidant content.

- Rice bran oil has a long history in Japan as a base for soaps and skin creams.

- In anti-aging oils because of its high antioxidant and gamma-oryzanol content. In Japan, women who use rice bran oil on their skin regularly are known as 'rice bran beauties', as their skin becomes very soft.

- Because of its softening properties, rice bran oil is excellent to add to hand creams.

- In massage oils for whole body massage because of its good lubricating and nourishing properties, without being sticky. It makes a soft and long massage oil. It blends well with jojoba oil.

- In eye care products that treat swollenness and puffiness around, and dark rings under, the eyes.

- In blends that treat all kinds of skin irritations and itchiness.

- In anti-cellulite oil blends together with a lighter oil such as sunflower.

- In hair packs for treating tired and structurally damaged hair. Always blend the rice bran oil with drier oils for this purpose.

- In sun care and protection products as the high tocotrienol content increases the efficacy of other ingredients in absorbing or reflecting UV rays. It has a natural sun protection factor (SPF) of 4.

- Due to its high antioxidant content, it works well as a base extraction oil for making macerated herb oils, e.g. calendula oil, St. John's wort oil, etc.

- In oil-based perfumes. For those who prefer to use non-alcohol based perfumes. Add 20-30% essential oils to rice bran oil. Rice bran oil absorbs and keeps the fragrance for a long time. Just a note of caution: the aroma of oil-based perfumes can easily be too heavy so be careful not to use too high a percentage of base note essential oils in the perfume. A good percentage guideline for using essential oils in perfumes is: base notes: 30%; middle notes: 20%; and top notes: 50%. Oil-based perfumes don't need to mature for the same length of time as alcohol-based perfumes, but the oil-based perfume is usually more mature after 2-3 weeks of making it.

- Gives the skin a matt finish.

- Excellent for tired-looking skin.

- Very good cooking oil. It has a high smoke point of +254°C/+490°F, so excellent for high temperature cooking such as stir-frying and deep frying. Its light flavour is perfect for salad dressings and baking.

Fatty Acid (Maximum) Content of Rice Bran Oil

Please note, as the percentages in the following illustration are for the maximum amount of fatty acid content found in rice bran oil, they may add up to more than 100%.

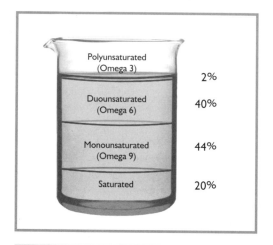

Polyunsaturated (Omega 3)	2%
Duounsaturated (Omega 6)	40%
Monounsaturated (Omega 9)	44%
Saturated	20%

Breakdown of Fatty Acid content of Rice Bran Oil	
Saturated	Palmitic Acid 12-13%
	Stearic Acid 2-3%
	Arachidic Acid ≤3%
	Myristic Acid ≤1%
Mono-unsaturated	Oleic Acid 20-42%
	Gadoleic Acid ≤2%
Duo-unsaturated	Linoleic Acid 36-40%
Poly-unsaturated	Linolenic Acid 1-2%

Rice Bran Oil Sample Recipes

These Recipes make 100ml.

Eye Oil

For treating swollen and puffy areas around the eyes.
40ml Rice Bran Oil
20ml Thistle Oil
20ml Rosehip Oil
6ml Hemp Seed Oil
5ml Evening Primrose Oil
5ml/g Vitamin E Oil (undiluted)
2ml Arnica Tincture
2ml/g Chamomile CO_2 Extract
5 drops Rosemary Antioxidant (CO_2 Extract)

Hair Oil for structurally damaged hair

30ml Rice Bran Oil
30ml Jojoba Oil
28ml Thistle Oil
5ml Calendula Oil
5ml/g Vitamin E Oil (undiluted)
1ml/g Vitamin A Palmitate
1ml (25 drops) Lavender Essential Oil
10 drops Sandalwood Essential Oil
5 drops Rosemary Antioxidant (CO_2 Extract)

Massage Oil for mature, dry skin

35ml Rice Bran Oil
33ml Thistle Oil
20ml Jojoba Oil
10ml Macadamia Nut Oil
2ml/g Vitamin E Oil (undiluted)

Massage Oil for sensitive skin

30ml Rice Bran Oil
20ml Jojoba Oil
20ml Apricot Kernel Oil
19ml Rosehip Oil
5ml Calendula Oil
4ml/g Vitamin E Oil (undiluted)
1ml/g Vitamin A Palmitate
1ml/g Chamomile CO_2 Extract
5 drops Rosemary Antioxidant (CO_2 Extract)

Skin Regeneration Face Oil

A regenerative blend. Suitable for all skin types, except oily skin.
20ml Rice Bran Oil
48ml Rosehip Oil
20ml Thistle Oil
10ml/g Vitamin E Oil (undiluted)
1ml/g Vitamin A Palmitate
1ml/g Sea Buckthorn CO_2 Extract
5 drops Rosemary Antioxidant (CO_2 Extract)

Percentages of Rice Bran Oil to use in products

Product	Product details	How much Oil you can use in the product	Average use
Sensitive/Dry/Mature Skin products	Face Oils	up to 50%	
	Whole Body Massage/Skin Oils for extra softness	up to 50%	30-35%
	Creams	up to 15%	8-10%
	Hand Creams for extra softness	up to 15%	8-10%
Skin Rejuvenation/ Anti-Aging products	Face Oils	up to 50%	
	Body Oils	up to 60%	
	Creams	up to 15%	8-10%
Around the Eye Care products	Eye Care Oils	up to 50%	
	Eye Creams	up to 8%	
Baby Care products	Everyday Baby Creams	up to 15%	12-15%
	Everyday Oil Blends	up to 40%	
Sun Care and Protection products	Before & After Face Sun Oils	up to 35%	
	Before & After Body Sun Oils	up to 50%	
	Sun Protection Lip Balms	Replace the Vegetable Oil/s in Lip Balm Recipes with Rice Bran Oil.	
	Sun Protection Creams and Lotions	up to 15%	10-12%
Hair Treatment products	Hair Oils and Hair Packs	up to 40%	
Anti-Cellulite products	Treatment Oils	up to 50%	
Perfumes	Oil-based Perfumes	up to 80%	70-80%

Table 32: Percentages of Rice Bran Oil to use in products

Rosehip Oil

Rosehip
INCI name: Rosa rubiginosa

Description

Rosa canina and *Rosa laevigata* are also used but *Rosa rubiginosa* produces a superior oil for skin care. In South America it is known as *Rosa mosqueta* or simply *Mosqueta*. The seeds contain approximately 9% oil. A dry to very dry and thin oil, which has a very soothing, moisturising and softening effect on the skin. Rosehip oil is the only vegetable oil, which contains natural tretinoin, the acid form of vitamin A also known as all-trans-retinoic acid or ATRA in quantities of 125mcg per every 100g. It is an excellent source of trans-retinoic acid (a natural precursor of vitamin A), which is also very good for treating all kinds of skin infections such as acne, pimples and boils. It is also useful in

the repair of damaged skin tissue caused by scalds, burns, varicose veins and skin over-exposed to sunlight, and for treating oily skin, sensitive skin, and reducing or healing fine lines around the eyes, wrinkles and scars. Rosehip is amongst the best vegetable oil source of omega 3 and is also a good source of omega 6, both essential fatty acids collectively known as vitamin F, involved in cellular membrane and tissue regeneration and normalising skin with large pores.

The SAP value for rosehip oil is unknown to me.

Absorption Note

Top.

Natural Vitamin Content

0.0001%, or 0.125mcg per 100ml of tretinoin, or vitamin A acid (see 'Description' above for further details); approximately 0.06%-0.09%, or 60-90mg per 100ml of rosehip oil of vitamin E (naturally-occurring d-alpha tocopherol).

Origin

Most commercial rosehip oil now comes from Chile and grows wild in the Southern Andes. Originally from southern Europe and Asia, it can also be found in north in different parts of USA and Canada. The plant was brought to South America in the 16th century by European immigrants to be used for ornamental purposes, and can be found in the Andean region of Argentina, in regions of Chile, and in some parts of Peru.

Shelf Life

Due to the high content of polyunsaturated fatty acids you should never buy rosehip oil, which does not have added vitamin E oil or other natural antioxidants, otherwise it will go rancid within 6 months. Adding 0.5% undiluted vitamin E oil, or an equivalent antioxidant, will increase the shelf life to 2 years.

Freezing Point

Under -15 °C (+5 °F).

Caution on the smell of Rosehip Oil in Skin Care products

Rosehip oil, especially the organic type, has a strong, distinct smell, which can become particularly unpleasant when blended with other raw materials to make a cream. This problem does not seem to really occur when rosehip oil is used in oil blends. I suggest that, when using rosehip oil in your recipes, especially for creams and lotions, to make it in small quantities first. If you're happy with the results you can make the product in larger quantities. If not, you can experiment with masking the smell with, for example, a base note essential oil, or using a different oil, or non-organic rosehip, as a substitute.

Further information

- Rosehip has a low melting point (under -15 °C/+5 °F), which helps, in the body, to counteract the high melting point of saturated fats such as cholesterol (178 °C/352 °F) or

cocoa butter (38 °C/100.4 °F), which is found in chocolate. Please see page 15 for information on 'Rebalancing certain skin types with vegetable oils'.

- See page 7 for 'More information on essential fatty acids (vitamin F)'.
- See page 29 for 'Tips for buying borage, camelina, evening primrose, hemp seed, kiwi seed and rosehip oils'.

Uses of Rosehip Oil

- Rosehip oil is a classic and luxurious vegetable oil, which is very effective for cell and tissue regeneration.
- Rosehip oil is excellent for treating sensitive and oily skin, skin with large pores as well as helping to treat all kinds of skin infections, such as acne, eczema, psoriasis, pimples and boils. It is also useful in the repair of damaged skin tissue caused by chemotherapy, scalds, burns, varicose veins and skin over-exposed to sunlight, skin pigmentation, and reducing or healing fine lines around the eyes, wrinkles and scars.
- It returns colour and life to damaged skin.
- Its consistency is dry to very dry and rosehip oil is considered to be one of the best anti-wrinkle oils available today. It soothes the fine wrinkles, especially around the eyes and mouth. It gives elasticity to the skin and helps against skin aging.
- In face oils. The oil has a short surface time on the skin, being rapidly absorbed by the skin and not leaving any fatty residue, which makes it an excellent face oil. It can also be used undiluted (100%).
- In massage oil blends. It is a long oil, which means that it can be used

for long strokes on the body, as well as being dry, which makes it good for short strokes on the face. This makes rosehip oil unique amongst the long oils, as all the other long oils are much fattier. The long oil that's closest to rosehip oil's dryness is jojoba oil. However, its dryness means that you have to mix it with fattier, more lubricating oils for whole body massage. Mixing it with grape seed oil is a good idea as this oil has similar properties but contains only 1% omega 3 essential fatty acids, unlike the rosehip oil, which contains up to 36%.

- In anti-wrinkle and skin rejuvenation face and skin oils and creams.
- If you want to make a lighter cream or lotion, rosehip oil is ideal.
- In before and after sun products. Rosehip is very healing for skin damaged by, or over-exposed to, ultraviolet radiation from the sun or x-ray radiation. Always add vitamin A and E oils to these products.
- In anti-cellulite oil blends.
- In oil blends for treating 'frozen' shoulder', also known as adhesive capsulitis, a condition that affects the shoulder joint capsule and results in stiffness and loss of movement in the shoulder joint.
- Because rosehip, along with apricot and peach kernel, are the classic oils for sensitive skin due to their softness and smoothness, use them together in oil blends and creams (for important information about using rosehip oil in creams, see the 'Caution on the smell of Rosehip Oil in Skin Care products').
- In baby products. Blend with fattier oils such as rice bran, avocado and apricot kernel for this purpose.

- In rheumatism and circulation treatment oil blends.
- In oil blends for healing bedsores.
- Can be used in hair treatment oils.
- Rosehip oil reduces the fattiness of other vegetable oils in blends.
- By adding rosehip oil to your skin, you reduce the overall melting point of fats in your skin, allowing the body to process them easier. (See 'Rebalancing certain skin types with vegetable oils' on page 15.)
- As a food supplement. The high quantity (25-36%) of alpha linolenic acid found in rosehip oil makes it a very good source of this omega 3 essential fatty acid and what I consider one of the most important sources of this vital nutrient for vegetarians.

Fatty Acid (Maximum) Content of Rosehip Oil

Please note, as the percentages in the illustration on the next page are for the maximum amount of fatty acid content found in rosehip oil, they may add up to more than 100%.

Breakdown of Fatty Acid content of Rosehip Oil	
Saturated	Palmitic Acid 3-8%
	Stearic Acid ≤2%
	Arachidic Acid <1%
Mono-unsaturated	Oleic Acid 13-19%
	Palmitoleic Acid <1%
	Eicosenoic Acid <1%
Duo-unsaturated	Linoleic Acid 44-48%
Poly-unsaturated	Alpha Linolenic Acid 25-36%

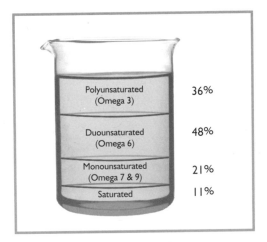

Polyunsaturated (Omega 3)	36%
Duounsaturated (Omega 6)	48%
Monounsaturated (Omega 7 & 9)	21%
Saturated	11%

Rosehip Oil Sample Recipes

These Recipes make 100ml.

Anti-Wrinkle Cure Oil for dry/ sensitive skin

85ml Rosehip Oil
13ml/g Vitamin E Oil (undiluted)
2ml/g Vitamin A Palmitate
5 drops Rosemary Antioxidant (CO_2 Extract)

Anti-Wrinkle Cure Oil for oily skin

60ml Rosehip Oil
20ml Evening Primrose Oil
10ml/g Vitamin E Oil (undiluted)
8ml Jojoba Oil
2ml/g Vitamin A Palmitate
5 drops Rosemary Antioxidant (CO_2 Extract)

Face Cure/Anti-Wrinkle Cure Oil for mature skin

70ml Rosehip Oil
9ml Macadamia Nut Oil
18ml/g Vitamin E Oil (undiluted)
2ml/g Vitamin A Palmitate
1ml/g Echium Seed CO_2 Extract
5 drops Rosemary Antioxidant (CO_2 Extract)

Face/Anti-Wrinkle Cure Oil for sensitive and large-pored skin

80ml Rosehip Oil
18ml/g Vitamin E Oil (undiluted)
2ml /g Vitamin A Palmitate
5 drops Rosemary Antioxidant (CO_2 Extract)

Face Serum for all skin types

78ml Rosehip Oil
20ml/g Vitamin E Oil (undiluted)
2ml/g Vitamin A Palmitate
5 drops Rosemary Antioxidant (CO_2 Extract)

Cellulite Treatment Oil Recipe 1

Rub in and massage into the skin daily.
27ml Rosehip Oil
27ml Borage Oil
27ml Thistle Oil
19ml/g Vitamin E Oil (undiluted)
5 drops Rosemary Antioxidant (CO_2 Extract)

Cellulite Treatment Oil Recipe 2

Rub in and massage into the skin daily.
60ml Rosehip Oil
30ml Macadamia Nut Oil
10ml/g Vitamin E Oil (undiluted)
5 drops Rosemary Antioxidant (CO_2 Extract)

Soothing Baby Oil

For general use. It's softening, calming and healing.
46ml Rosehip Oil
40ml Apricot Kernel Oil
10ml Calendula Oil
3ml/g Vitamin E Oil (undiluted)
1ml/g Chamomile CO_2 Extract

Rosehip Acne Treatment Oil

Apply every evening.

61.5ml Rosehip Oil
10ml Borage Oil
10ml Jojoba Oil
10ml/g Vitamin E Oil (undiluted)
5ml Thistle Oil
2ml/g Vitamin A Palmitate
1.5ml Aromantic's Anti-Acne Active Formula
5 drops Rosemary Antioxidant (CO_2 Extract)

Daily Rheumatism/Arthritis Treatment Oil

50ml Rosehip Oil
50ml Borage Oil
10 drops Rosemary Antioxidant (CO_2 Extract)

Scar Tissue Treatment Oil

For general use. Apply up to twice a day.

25ml Rosehip Oil
25ml Borage Oil
50ml/g Vitamin E Oil (undiluted)
10 drops Rosemary Antioxidant (CO_2 Extract)

Sunscreen

For protecting the skin. Use daily before exposure to the sun for a maximum of 2 weeks.

25ml Rosehip Oil
20ml Thistle Oil
50ml/g Vitamin E Oil (undiluted)
5ml/g Vitamin A Palmitate
10 drops Rosemary Antioxidant (CO_2 Extract)

Percentages of Rosehip Oil to use in products

Product	Product details	How much Oil you can use in the product	Average use
Skin Rejuvenation/ Anti-Wrinkle/Anti-Aging products	Anti-Wrinkle Creams	up to 10%	6-8%
	Anti-Wrinkle Face Oils/Serums	up to 85%	
	Rejuvenating Body Oils	up to 35%	
Creams for sensitive skin	Everyday Creams for sensitive & dry skin	up to 10%	4-6%
	Everyday Creams for sensitive & oily skin	up to 7%	5-6%
Acne Treatment products	Treatment Creams	up to 12%	6-8%
	Treatment Oils	up to 65%	
Eczema and Psoriasis Treatment products	Treatment Creams	up to 10%	5-6%
	Treatment Oils	up to 65%	

/contd

contd/

Product	Product details	How much Oil you can use in the product	Average use
Sun Care and Protection products	Before-Sun Oils	up to 40%	
	After-Sun Oils	up to 60%	
	Sunburn Treatment Oils (not on open wounds but rather apply on area around the wound)	up to 70%	
	Sun Creams	up to 12%	6-8%
Baby products	Everyday Baby Creams	up to 10%	5-7%
	Nappy Rash Treatment Oils	up to 50%	
Hair Treatment products	Everyday use Hair Treatment Oils	up to 20%	
	Hair/Scalp Cure Treatment Oils	up to 80%	
X-ray radiation/Sun Eczema Treatment products	Treatment Oils	up to 45%	
Skin Tissue Treatment products	Scar Tissue Oil Blends	up to 50%	25%
	Oil Treatment Blends for treating damaged skin tissue	30-50%	
Anti-Cellulite products	Treatment Oils	up to 60%	
Frozen Shoulder Treatment products	Treatment Oils	up to 60%	
Varicose Veins Treatment products	Treatment Oils	up to 40%	
	Treatment Gels	up to 50%	
Bedsore Treatment products	Treatment Oils (never on open wounds but can be applied on area around the wound)	up to 30%	
Rheumatism Treatment products	Treatment Oils	up to 50%	
Circulation Treatment products	Treatment Oils	up to 80%	

Table 33: Percentages of Rosehip Oil to use in products

Sesame Oil

Sesame

INCI name: Sesamum indicum

Description

A half-fatty oil with a light yellow-gold colour and a subtle pleasant sesame taste and smell. It is important to note that I do not recommend the toasted sesame oil generally sold for cooking, as it should not be used on the skin. I recommend only the cold pressed oil for use in skin care products. The seed contains 50% oil, which is extracted by crushing and cold pressing and then filtering the resulting oil. It has good skin care properties for sun oils as it naturally contains sun protection factor (SPF) 2-3 in the oil. Used safely for baby and adult massage. Also widely used for culinary purposes. The phenolic substance sesamol works as an antioxidant and keeps the oil fresh for a long time.

The SAP value for sesame oil is 133g.

Absorption Note

Middle.

Natural Vitamin Content

0.02-0.05%, or 20-50mg per 100ml of sesame oil of vitamin E (naturally-occurring d-alpha tocopherol).

Origin

Originally from the Middle East, North Africa and India, Sesame is grown in many parts of the world. The biggest area of production is currently believed to be India, but the crop is also grown in China, Burma, Ethiopia and in South and North America. The biggest organic producers today are Sudan and Burkina Faso.

Shelf Life

2-3 years (due to its high content of oleic acid and the phenolic substance known as sesamol).

Freezing Point

-3 to -6°C (+26.6 to +21.2°F).

Uses of Sesame Oil

- Sesame oil is softening and nourishing (due to its high omega 6 essential fatty acid content), so it makes a good skin oil.

- It can be used on a range of skin types, from dry to oily skin.

- It is absorbed quite slowly by the skin and offers good lubrication. As it is a long oil, it is good for long strokes massage used in whole body massages. By adding melted coconut butter to the massage oil you can make it thicker for added glide.

- Add it to protective oil blends and creams as the waxes in the oil provide good protection.

- It is also beneficial in sun care products because it has a natural sun protection factor (SPF) of 2-4 due to its sesamol content.

- Excellent for restoring cuticles and nails.

- Sesame oil is also very effective as nose drops for quick relief of dried nasal membranes caused by cold winds and central heating. In Sweden it is certified as a natural drug for this use.

- Ayurvedic medicine considers sesame oil as 'the' vegetable oil cleanser and is often used in the treatment of psoriasis and eczema.

- Used extensively in India as a healing oil. Ayurvedic practitioners use it in a variety of ways for the treatment of various chronic diseases, including rheumatic pain. They tend to heat up the oil to blood temperature before using it and this makes it thinner and easier to work with and also speeds up the absorption time by the skin.

- It is naturally antibacterial and antifungal. Studies in USA have showed that students rinsing their mouths with sesame oil reduce 85% of mouth bacteria, which cause gingivitis. Sesame oil is also commonly used in the Ayurvedic therapy called oil-pulling or oil swishing, which is said to speed up cell metabolism in the body, thereby helping to heal and rejuvenate the body.

- In Sweden, it is used a topical application for broken capillary veins.

- As it is relatively odour free it is often used in the production of perfumes.

- In ointments, balms and lip balms.

- As a base extraction oil to make macerated herbal oils.

- Due to its high lechitin content, you can use it as a help emulsifier. See 'Uses' in sunflower oil

- An excellent culinary oil, which is used as a salad dressing and for stir-frying. It has a smoke point of $+177°C/+350°F$. Please note again that we do not recommend the use of toasted sesame oil generally sold for cooking, as it should not be used on the skin.

Tips for using heated Sesame Oil

If you want to heat the sesame oil before using it, you can put the amount you need in a plastic bottle and heat under a running hot tap. This saves the oil from being heated too many times.

Fatty Acid (Maximum) Content of Sesame Oil

Please note, as the percentages in the illustration on the next page are for the maximum amount of fatty acid content found in sesame oil, they may add up to more than 100%.

Breakdown of Fatty Acid content of Sesame Oil	
Saturated	Palmitic Acid 7-11%
	Stearic Acid 4-6%
	Arachidic Acid <1%
	Behenic Acid <0.5%

Mono-unsaturated	Oleic Acid 36-46%
	Palmitoleic Acid <0.5%
	Eicosenoic Acid <0.5%
Duo-unsaturated	Linoleic Acid 38-45%
Poly-unsaturated	Alpha Linolenic Acid 1-1.5%

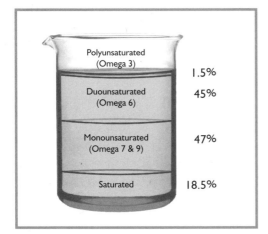

Polyunsaturated (Omega 3) — 1.5%
Duounsaturated (Omega 6) — 45%
Monounsaturated (Omega 7 & 9) — 47%
Saturated — 18.5%

Sesame Oil Sample Recipes

The Recipes make 100ml.

Nail & Cuticle Oil

79ml Sesame Oil
10ml Peach Kernel Oil
10ml/g Vitamin E Oil (undiluted)
1ml Vitamin A Palmitate
5 drops Rosemary Antioxidant (CO_2 Extract)

Nose Drops

Apply with a cotton bud a few times a day.
85ml Sesame Oil
9ml Rosehip Oil
5ml Vitamin E Oil
1ml Vitamin A Palmitate
5 drops Rosemary Antioxidant (CO_2 Extract)

Massage Oil for dry, mature or sensitive skin

43ml Sesame Oil
5ml Castor Oil
15ml Coconut Butter (melt first in a bain-marie and then add to the blend)
30ml Peach Kernel Oil
5ml Rosehip Oil
2ml/g Vitamin E Oil (undiluted)

Before Sun Oil

55ml Sesame Oil
15ml Sunflower Oil
10ml Shea Butter Oil
10ml Jojoba Oil
10ml Vitamin E Oil (undiluted)
5 drops Rosemary Antioxidant (CO_2 Extract)

Protective Baby Oil

Apply 1-2 times a day.
45ml Sesame Oil
20ml Peach Kernel Oil
15ml Rosehip Oil
15ml Jojoba Oil
5ml/g Vitamin E Oil (undiluted)
5 drops Rosemary Antioxidant (CO_2 Extract)

Soothing Baby Oil

Apply 1-2 times a day.
35ml Sesame Oil
30ml Apricot Kernel Oil
10g Shea Butter ((melt first in a bain-marie and then add to the blend))
10ml Rosehip Oil
10ml Jojoba Oil
5ml/g Vitamin E Oil
5 drops Rosemary Antioxidant (CO_2 Extract)

Percentages of Sesame Oil to use in products

Product	Product details	How much Oil you can use in the product	Average use
Massage products	Whole Body Massage Oils	up to 50%	
Face Oils		up to 20%	
Body Oils		up to 40%	
Skin Protection products	Protective Ointments	up to 50%	
	Hand Creams	Up to 10% - combine with Jojoba Oil for added protection.	6-8%
Psoriasis and Eczema Treatment products	Treatment Creams	up to 10%	2-4%
	Treatment Oils	up to 30%	
Oil-Pulling		100%	
Nose Drops		100%	
Baby products	Everyday Baby Oils	up to 40%	
Nail Care products	Cuticle Creams	up to 15%	8-10%
	Nail/Cuticle Oils	30-90%	
Sun Protection and Care products	Creams	up to 16%	10-12%
	Oils	up to 50%	

Table 34: Percentages of Sesame Oil to use in products

Shea Butter Oil

Shea
INCI name: Butyrospermum parkii

Description

The shea tree grows wild on the savannah in several of the West African countries like Ghana, Nigeria and Mali. The tree can grow to be 20-25 metres high and has deep roots (20 metres), enabling it to withstand long periods of drought. The first fruits appear after 8-12 years and peak productivity is reached when the tree is about 40 years old although it can continue to bear fruit for up to 150 years. Each tree produces approximately 50kg of fruit every year. The shea tree's fruit (and its stone, or nut) is an important raw material for West Africa and for hundreds of years the local people have used it for food, medicinal, decorative and cosmetic purposes and as a protection against the sun and bad weather. Most of the shea nuts are now exported to Europe where they are cleaned and pressed. You get approximately 8% butter from the fruit, which is commonly (and confusingly) called a shea nut. Reducing the amount of stearic acid in the shea butter produces shea butter oil. The shea butter cools down so they can remove the stearic acid. The shea butter contains 5-10% phytosterols, which stimulate cell growth.

The SAP value for shea butter oil is 128g.

Absorption Note
Base.

Natural Vitamin Content
Traces of naturally occurring vitamin E.

Origin
The tree grows on the savannah from Gambia in West Africa to Uganda in East Africa.

Shelf Life
2-year shelf life.

Freezing Point
+5 to +15°C (+41 to +59°F).

Uses of Shea Butter Oil

- A very fatty oil used in creams, sun creams, body butters, lotions and massage oils. Good for moisturising,

162

protecting and healing the skin, especially dry and damaged skin. It has mildly antibacterial and anti-inflammatory properties, good moisture-retaining properties and protects the skin from the sun and from drying out.

- Shea butter oil is known to be a good carrier of different active and healing ingredients, which are released more quickly than in other oils and fats.

- Shea butter oil is well tolerated by nearly everyone but be more careful with the use of shea butter oil for certain skin types and problems, such as acne, oily skin and large pores. The use of the oil for these conditions and types can enlarge as well as clog the pores.

- However, shea butter oil is especially good for dry, sensitive, baby, and black skin care.

- It seems to be a particularly good skin emollient and moisturiser for people from Africa or the West Indies as their skin needs the type of fattiness that shea butter products offer.

- It is also good for dry skin prone to eczema and psoriasis.

- It is suitable for preventing or treating stretch marks during and after pregnancy. Women in West Africa use the solid shea butter on the their stomachs during pregnancy to avoid stretch marks and this is very effective because of the phytosterol content. I consider shea butter more healing than the oil but quite often it is more convenient to use the oil.

- Shea butter oil has a natural sun protection factor of 2-3, due to the high content of cinnamic acid esters present in the oil, which are also found in chemically produced sun protection products. It also enhances pigmentation. Add to after-sun products for it's healing effects.

- The cinnamic acid is responsible for the healing, anti-inflammatory effects of the product, whilst the phytosterol content stimulates the formation and growth of new cells, helping the skin to heal more quickly than normal. Phytosterols have constituents that are typical in adaptogens. Adaptogens are claimed to be unique from other substances in their ability to have a normalising effect on the body by balancing endocrine hormones and the immune system, and helping the body to maintain optimal homeostasis. Adaptogens are also protective and raise an individual's resistance to physical, chemical, or biological stresses.

- Use for the treatment of scar tissue but always blend it with both vitamin E oil as well as a thinner oil for this purpose.

- In hair care products for dry hair or dry and irritated scalp.

- In massage blends for whole body massage as it is very slowly absorbed by the skin. Helps the hands glide well over the skin.

- In skin care products it has good anti-inflammatory properties and is useful for treating smaller wounds and skin infections.

- It has excellent softening properties making the skin soft and supple.

- It also gives body to massage oils.

- Shea butter oil is also used as cooking oil.

Fatty Acid (Maximum) Content of Shea Butter Oil

Please note, as the percentages in the following illustration are for the maximum amount of fatty acid content found in shea butter oil, they may add up to more than 100%.

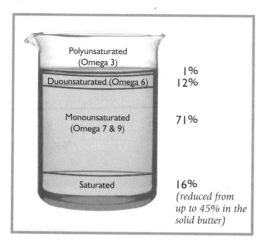

Polyunsaturated (Omega 3)	1%
Duounsaturated (Omega 6)	12%
Monounsaturated (Omega 7 & 9)	71%
Saturated	16% (reduced from up to 45% in the solid butter)

Breakdown of Fatty Acid content of Shea Butter Oil	
Saturated	Palmitic Acid 6%
	Stearic Acid 10%
Mono-unsaturated	Oleic Acid 70%
	Palmitoleic Acid 1%
Duo-unsaturated	Linoleic Acid 12%
Poly-unsaturated	Alpha Linolenic Acid ≤1%

Shea Butter Oil Sample Recipes

These Recipes make 100ml.

Before Sun Oil

30ml Shea Butter Oil

30ml Sesame Oil

30ml Sunflower Oil

10ml/g Vitamin E Oil (undiluted)

5 drops Rosemary Antioxidant (CO_2 Extract)

Scar Tissue Treatment Oil

30ml Shea Butter Oil

30ml Borage Oil

40ml/g Vitamin E Oil (undiluted)

10 drops Rosemary Antioxidant (CO_2 Extract)

Stretch Mark Treatment Oil Recipe 1

10g Shea Butter Oil

30ml Thistle Oil

30ml Borage Oil

30ml/g Vitamin E Oil (undiluted)

10-15 drops Essential Oils

8 drops Rosemary Antioxidant (CO_2 Extract)

Stretch Mark Treatment Oil Recipe 2

50ml Shea Butter Oil

20ml Thistle Oil

15ml Borage Oil

15ml/g Vitamin E Oil (undiluted)

4 drops Rosemary Antioxidant (CO_2 Extract)

Stretch Mark Treatment Oil Recipe 3

40ml Shea Butter Oil

25ml Rosehip Oil

15ml Evening Primrose Oil

10ml Comfrey Oil

10ml/g Vitamin E Oil (undiluted)

4 drops Rosemary Antioxidant (CO_2 Extract)

Stretch Mark Ointment

Stage 1
50ml Shea Butter Oil
10g Mango Butter
10g Beeswax

Stage 2
25ml Thistle Oil

Stage 3
5ml/g Vitamin E Oil (undiluted)
10-15 drops Essential Oils

Method

1) Melt all of the stage 1 ingredients in a bain-marie.

2) When the mixture has completely melted, add stage 2 ingredients, while whisking all of the time. To speed up the cooling process put the bowl in a basin of cold water while whisking around the edges of the bowl - make sure that no water from the basin splashes into the bowl.

3) When the mixture has become the consistency of thick soup, stir in the Stage 3 ingredients.

4) Pour into jars and label.

Baby Skin Healing Oil

40ml Shea Butter Oil
20ml Rosehip Oil
10ml Thistle Oil
10ml Evening Primrose Oil
10ml St. John's Wort Oil
4ml Calendula Oil
5ml/g Vitamin E Oil (undiluted)
1ml/g Sea Buckthorn CO_2 Extract
5 drops Rosemary Antioxidant (CO_2 Extract)

Massage Oil for dry and sensitive skin

For Swedish massage or whole body massage.
35ml Shea Butter Oil
34ml Jojoba Oil
30ml Thistle Oil
1ml/g Vitamin E Oil (undiluted)

Hair Treatment Oil for dry hair or dry, irritated scalp

35ml Shea Butter Oil
40ml Thistle Oil
20ml Calendula Oil
5ml/g Vitamin E Oil (undiluted)
5 drops Rosemary Antioxidant (CO_2 Extract)

Black Hair Oil

60ml Shea Butter Oil
20ml Thistle Oil
15ml Calendula Oil
5ml/g Vitamin E Oil (undiluted)
5 drops Rosemary Antioxidant (CO_2 Extract)

Rejuvenating Skin Oil for black skin

25ml Shea Butter Oil
20ml Avocado Oil
20ml Kiwi Seed Oil
20ml Thistle Oil
15ml/g Vitamin E Oil (undiluted)
5 drops Rosemary Antioxidant (CO_2 Extract)

Percentages of Shea Butter Oil to use in products

Product	Product details	How much Oil you can use in the product	Average use
Stretch Mark Treatment products	Treatment Oils for during/after pregnancy	Up to 70% - always add Vitamin E Oil.	
Scar Tissue Treatment products	Treatment Oils	up to 50%	
Massage products	Whole Body Massage Oil Blends	up to 50%	
Skin Rejuvenation/Anti-Wrinkle products	Face Oils/Serums (not for oily or large-pored skin).	Up to 30% - remember to blend with drier, thinner Oils such as Rosehip Oil.	
Lip products	Lip Balms	Up to 10% in your Recipes - replace the other Oils in the Recipes.	5-10%
Eczema and Psoriasis Treatment products	General Healing/Treatment Creams	up to 8%	5-6%
	Treatment Oils	up to 20%	
Sun Care and Protection products	Before Sun Creams	up to 8%	5-6%
	Before Sun Oil	up to 40%	
	After Sun Creams	up to 12%	8-10%
	After Sun Treatment Oils	up to 50%	
Hair Care and Treatment products	Hair Treatment Oil for dry hair/dry, irritated scalp	up to 40%	
	Black Hair Care Oil	up to 60%	
Creams	Everyday Creams for dry, or sensitive skin	up to 15%	7-9%
	Hand Creams	up to 15%	8-10%
	Foot Creams	up to 15%	10-12%
Psoriasis and Eczema products	Treatment Creams	up to 10%	6-8%
Baby products	Everyday Baby Creams	up to 15%	10-12%
	Baby Ointments	up to 50%	15-25%
	Everyday Baby Oils	up to 50%	

Table 35: Percentages of Shea Butter Oil to use in products

St. John's Wort Oil

St. John's Wort

INCI name: Hypericum perforatum and usually the INCI name for the oil that the St. John's wort is macerated in.

Description

This is a macerated herbal oil, which has a dark, reddish-brown colour from the hypericin found in the flowers. You can see the hypericin in the petals, as it looks like tiny, blood-coloured islands on the yellow-orange petals. The flowers or just-opened buds are usually used in macerated oils. It is the hypericin content that gives the oil its characteristic reddish-brown colour, particularly if olive oil was used for the maceration process. However, many of the St. John's wort oils available for purchasing are a green colour because the whole plant was used for extraction/maceration, meaning that the chlorophyll content

was increased while the hypericin content is proportionally lower. The herb is named for St. John the Baptist, and the word 'wort' comes from an old English word meaning 'root'. Sometimes called the 'sunshine herb', it has a 2400-year history of safe and effective usage in folk, herbal, and ancient medicine. Hipppocrates himself prescribed *hypericum* as medicine. In ancient Greece, St. John's wort was used to treat many ailments, including sciatica, fever, and poisonous reptile bites. In Europe, St. John's wort was used by herbalists for the topical treatment of wounds and burns. It is also a folk remedy for kidney and lung ailments, as well as for depression. Ancient Europeans believed that it had magical protective powers against disease and evil.

For the SAP value, refer to the oil that the St. John's wort has been macerated in.

Natural Vitamin Content

Refer to the vegetable oil that the St. John's wort is macerated in.

Origin

Indigenous to the United Kingdom, France, USA and other countries.

Shelf Life

Refer to the oil that the St. John's wort has been macerated in.

Freezing Point

Refer to the oil that the St. John's wort has been macerated in.

Contraindications. Important, please read before using St. John's Wort

St. John's wort oil is never added to before sun or sun tanning products because, while St. John's Wort Oil is soothing to the skin, it also makes the skin photosensitive. This means that the skin shouldn't be exposed to the sun after St. John's wort has been applied externally in the form of an ointment, oil, cream, compress or lotion. Even taking it internally may make fair-skinned people more sensitive to the sun. Hypericin promotes blood circulation in the skin and activates the finer capillaries.

For more information

- See page 6 for 'Macerated oils'.
- See page 29 for how to make an oil compress.

Fatty Acid (Maximum) Content of St. John's Wort Oil

Refer to the fatty acid chart and breakdown table of the oil that the St. John's wort oil has been macerated in.

Use of St. John's Wort herb as an antidepressant, calming nerve tonic

- In more recent times, St. John's wort achieved instant fame in the USA and in Europe when clinical studies confirmed its effectiveness in the treatment of mild-to-moderate depression. The news came as no surprise to herbalists, who have long prescribed St. John's wort not only for depression, but also for the treatment of wounds, burns, injured nerves, inflammations, ulcers, anxiety, and other ailments.

- In Germany, more than fifty percent of depression, anxiety, and sleep disorders are treated with St. John's wort. According to Norman Rosenthal, the author of *St. John's Wort: The Herbal Way to Feeling Good*, St. John's wort enjoys many times the sales than Prozac.

- The herb has also been shown to help people with seasonal affective disorder (SAD), a common form of depression believed to be caused by lack of light during autumn and winter. Research suggests that St. John's wort has potential in the treatment of premenstrual syndrome (PMS), obsessive-compulsive disorder, menopause symptoms, and viral infections.

- St. John's wort contains about fifty active constituents, but research indicates that the pigment, hypericin, which is found in the flowers, is the ingredient that helps ease depression. Numerous studies show that hypericin appears to act similar to drugs that are monamine oxidase (MAO) inhibitors and selective serotonin-reuptake inhibitors, elevating mood and acting as a mild sedative.

Use of St. John's Wort in Skin Care

- St. John's wort soothes irritations of the skin; with generally beneficial effects as the herb has calming properties. St. John's wort is mostly used externally in the form of macerated herbal oil, an infusion or tincture, but these preparations are increasingly being added to creams, lotions and ointments.

- In antiviral/anti-inflammatory and healing ointments, creams, treatment oils or gels for its antiviral, antibacterial, anti-inflammatory and astringent properties. These products can be used for the treatment of first degree burns, sunburn, cuts, scrapes, bruises, boils, minor skin irritations and inflammations, eczema, rheumatic and muscular aches and pains associated with the nervous system e.g. myalgia or shingles and associated rashes and blisters. Also used for soothing the pain, burning and itching of haemorrhoids. For itchy skin conditions, add chickweed infusion to the cream. For sunburn and burns, mix the St. John's wort oil with calendula oil. For bruises, blend St. John's wort oil with arnica oil/tincture and comfrey oil.

- As a treatment oil for herpes simplex, apply St. John's wort oil to the lips. Also add tea tree and lavender essential oils and vitamin E oil.

- Excellent for products for sensitive skin, easily irritated skin and infected acne or spots. Use as a treatment or bath oil but use with caution for acne skin as the oil mostly has an olive oil base and as such is very oily. Mix it with drier oils for this purpose. For bath oils blend it with turkey red oil (saponified castor oil).

- Excellent for all skin problems or conditions that react positively to exposure to the sun, such as eczema and psoriasis.

- In after sun products such as creams, gels and treatment oils for its soothing effects. For sunburn and burns, mix the St. John's wort oil with calendula oil and, preferably, aloe vera gel.

- The oil is heated up for a warming effect to use in compresses and treatment and massage oils to relieve stiff and tense muscles, neuro-inflammations, sciatica, and back pain. Unheated St. John's wort oil is used in compresses; and treatment and massage oils for a cooling effect, which is appropriate when stretching pinched or cramped muscles and easing pain.

- In baby products for calming nappy rashes, sensitive or inflamed skin. Good for using in the evening before sleep because of its soothing properties.

- Be aware that the oil imparts a reddish colour to oil blends and creams.

St. John's Wort Oil Sample Recipes

These Recipes make 100ml.

Itchy Skin Treatment Oil

35ml St. John's Wort Oil
35ml Rosehip Oil
20ml Evening Primrose Oil
7ml/g Vitamin E Oil (undiluted)
1ml/g Vitamin A Palmitate
2ml/g Chamomile CO_2 Extract
5 drops Rosemary Antioxidant (CO_2 Extract)

Bruise Treatment Oil

Apply to bruised area.
30ml St. John's Wort Oil
25ml Comfrey Oil
23ml Rosehip Oil
10ml Arnica Oil
10ml/g Vitamin E Oil (undiluted)
2ml/g Chamomile CO_2 Extract
5 drops Rosemary Antioxidant (CO_2 Extract)

Everyday Acne Treatment Oil

For calming infected skin/spots.
15ml St. John's Wort Oil
70ml Rosehip Oil
5ml Calendula Oil
8ml/g Vitamin E Oil (undiluted)
1ml/g Vitamin A Palmitate
1ml/g Chamomile CO_2 Extract
5 drops Rosemary Antioxidant (CO_2 Extract)

Everyday Baby Oil

35ml St. John's Wort Oil
30ml Calendula Oil
30ml Rosehip Oil
5ml/g Vitamin E Oil (undiluted)
5 drops Rosemary Antioxidant (CO_2 Extract)

Whole Body Massage Oil for dry or sensitive skin

Very calming and relaxing massage oil for whole body massage.
40ml St. John's Wort Oil
20ml Jojoba Oil
20ml Apricot Kernel Oil
18ml Rosehip Oil
2ml/g Vitamin E Oil (undiluted)

After Sun Oil

30ml St. John's Wort Oil
20ml Calendula Oil
20ml Borage Oil
15ml Thistle Oil
15ml/g Vitamin E Oil (undiluted)
5 drops Rosemary Antioxidant (CO_2 Extract)

Percentages of St. John's Wort Oil to use in products

Product	Product details	How much Oil you can use in the product	Average use
After Sun Care products	After Sun Creams	up to 15%	
	After Sun Oil Treatments. This Oil will lower the skin temperature.	up to 50%	
Products that treat sunburn, burns (first degree), bruises, itchiness and skin irritations	Treatment Creams	up to 20%	12-15%
	Treatment Oils	up to 50%	
	Ointments	up to 70%	
Psoriasis and Eczema products	Treatment Creams	up to 20%	10-12%
	Treatment Oils	up to 50%	
Products that treat sensitive, easily infected skin e.g. acne-prone skin	Treatment Creams	up to 10%	5-6%
	Sensitive Skin Treatment Oils	up to 40%	
	Acne Treatment Oils	up to 20%	

/contd

/contd

Bath products	Bath Oils	Up to 30% - can blend with Turkey Red Bath Oil.	
Baby products	Nappy Rash Creams	up to 15%	10-12%
	Before-Sleep Soothing and calming Oils	up to 100%	
	Treatment Oils	up to 40%	
Pain relief products	Treatment Oils for aches and pains	up to 60%	
	Shingles Treatment Oil	up to 100%	

Table 36: Percentages of St. John's Wort Oil to use in products

Sunflower Oil

Sunflower
INCI name: Helianthus anuus

Description

Sunflower seeds contain 40-50% oil, which is thin, dry, runny and light yellow, reminiscent of thistle oil, but fattier. The raw oil has a strong smell and taste, which is removed during the extraction process. It is a dry oil containing a high level of linoleic acid (omega 6 essential fatty acid). It spreads easily and is absorbed relatively quickly by the skin. Sunflower oil has been used for cooking for a very long time but the cold pressed sunflower oil has a low smoke point (+109°C/+228°F), so its best not used for cooking but it is perfect for making salad dressings and mayonnaise.

The SAP value for sunflower oil is 134g.

Absorption Note
Middle.

Natural Vitamin Content
0.035%-0.075%, or 35-75mg per 100ml of vitamin E (natural alpha tocopherol); and traces of vitamin K.

Origin
Originates in Mexico but these days it mostly comes from Europe.

Shelf Life
Keeps for 1.5-2 years.

Freezing Point
-16 to -18°C (+3.2 to +0.4°F).

For more information

- See 'Essential fatty acids (vitamin F)' on page 7 for more information.
- See page 29 for how to make an oil compress.

Uses of Sunflower Oil

- I recommend the use of sunflower oil in all kinds of skin care products due to the high content (up to 70%) of linoleic acid, an omega 6 essential fatty acid.
- Sunflower has a nourishing effect on the skin.
- It can be used for all skin types, even oily skin as it is a dry oil. It also has

excellent pore-reduction qualities, so good to use on large-pored skin.

- In acne, eczema and psoriasis treatment products.
- In products that treat haemorrhoids.
- Its high linoleic acid content makes it good for treating skin bruises and leg ulcers.
- Sunflower oil spreads well and is absorbed relatively quickly without leaving a sticky feeling, which makes it an excellent oil to add to skin and massage oil blends. So, when using it in massage oil blends, I recommended blending it with fattier, softer and longer oils such as avocado, apricot kernel, peach kernel, sweet almond oil or better still, olive oil, to provide better lubrication. Sunflower oil is not soft on the skin, it is in fact a little rough and half-long.
- In cellulite oil blends.
- In hair care products it is used to treat seborrhoea and structurally damaged hair.
- Bath oil blends.
- To give homemade soap extra softness.
- Adding sunflower oil to creams and lotions will make them lighter and drier. The high lecithin content of sunflower oil makes it a good choice for making creams and lotions as lecithin helps to emulsify in the same way that egg yolks, which contain 8-10% lecithin, help to emulsify oils and eggs to make mayonnaise. So, sunflower oil is therefore excellent for adding to vegetal creams, or to recipes that you find difficult to make thick enough, or to recipes where you find that the cream separates easily.

- The presence of sunflower oil in a product helps active ingredients in products to be absorbed more quickly into the skin, thereby enhancing their effect.
- Sunflower oil is a good cooking oil but the cold pressed (unrefined) oil should not be used in high temperature cooking.
- Psychological benefit of sunflower oil: I don't usually talk about the psychological benefits of the oils but sunflower oil is special in a sense. Imagine a sunflower field in the sun. All of the flowers are turned toward the sun and their faces follow the sun as it changes direction across the sky during the day. All of the flowers beam their beautiful strong yellow petals out towards the sun. No wonder that the oil produced from these sun-loving plants has a high content of vitamin F, which makes it an excellent ingredient in any uplifting oil blends for the skin and body.

Fatty Acid (Maximum) Content of Sunflower Oil

Please note, as the percentages below are for the maximum amount of fatty acid content found in sunflower oil, they may add up to more than 100%.

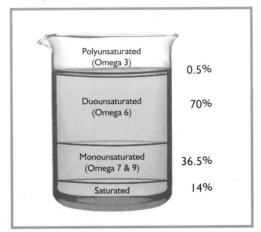

Polyunsaturated (Omega 3)	0.5%
Duounsaturated (Omega 6)	70%
Monounsaturated (Omega 7 & 9)	36.5%
Saturated	14%

Breakdown of Fatty Acid content of Sunflower Oil	
Saturated	Palmitic Acid 4-7%
	Stearic Acid 2-4%
	Arachidic Acid 1-1.5%
	Myristic Acid <0.5%
	Behenic Acid <1%
Mono-unsaturated	Oleic Acid 15-35%
	Palmitoleic Acid ≤1%
	Eicosenoic Acid <0.5%
Duo-unsaturated	Linoleic Acid 55-70%
Poly-unsaturated	Alpha Linolenic Acid <0.5%

Sunflower Oil Sample Recipes

These Recipes make 100ml.

Anti-Wrinkle Face Oil/Serum for dry or sensitive Skin

40ml Sunflower Oil
10ml Thistle Oil
30ml Rosehip Oil
5ml Evening Primrose Oil
15ml Vitamin E Oil (undiluted)
5 drops Rosemary Antioxidant (CO_2 Extract)

Cellulite Massage Oil

50ml Sunflower Oil
18ml Jojoba Oil
10ml Avocado Oil
10ml Thistle Oil
10ml/g Vitamin E Oil (undiluted)
15 drops Grapefruit Essential Oil
10 drops Lemon Essential Oil
10 drops Rosemary Essential Oil
5 drops Juniper Essential Oil
5 drops Rosemary Antioxidant (CO_2 Extract)

Massage Oil for dry or sensitive Skin

40ml Sunflower Oil
20ml Avocado Oil
20ml Apricot Oil
10ml Rosehip Oil
9ml Jojoba Oil
1ml/g Vitamin E Oil (undiluted)

Uplifting Face Oil

40ml Sunflower Oil
38ml Rosehip Oil
7ml Pumpkin Seed Oil
15ml Vitamin E Oil (undiluted)
5 drops Rosemary Antioxidant (CO_2 Extract)

Everyday Acne Treatment Oil

30ml Sunflower Oil
30ml Rosehip Oil
27ml Evening Primrose Oil
10ml/g Vitamin E Oil (undiluted)
1.5ml/g Vitamin A Palmitate
1.5ml Aromantic's Anti-Acne Active Formula
5 drops Rosemary Antioxidant (CO_2 Extract)

Computer Face Oil

For people sitting in front of the computer. They need the sun from the sunflower and calendula and the gamma linolenic acid (GLA) from the borage!

40ml Sunflower Oil
25ml Rosehip Oil
10ml Borage Oil
5ml Calendula Oil
5ml Pumpkin Seed Oil
15ml/g Vitamin E Oil (undiluted)
5 drops Rosemary Antioxidant (CO_2 Extract)

Percentages of Sunflower Oil to use in products

Product	Product details	How much Oil you can use in the product	Average use
Circulation Enhancement products	For treating circulation problems in the legs and feet	up to 50%	
Acne Treatment products	Treatment Creams	up to 15%	6-8%
	Treatment Oils	up to 40%	
Eczema and Psoriasis Treatment products	Treatment Creams	up to 12%	5-7%
Creams	To make Creams and Lotion lighter and drier	up to 15%	10-12%
	For oily/large-pored skin	up to 8%	3-5%
Massage products	Whole Body Massage Oil Blends	up to 40%	
Skin Rejuvenation/ Anti-Wrinkle products	Face Oils/Serums	up to 40%	
	Body Oils	up to 50%	
	Creams	up to 15%	8-10%
Elderly/sagging skin Treatment products	Treatment Creams	up to 20%	12-15%
	Treatment Oils	up to 50%	40-50%
Anti-Cellulite products	Anti-Cellulite Oil Blends	60%	
Hair Care products	Hair Oil Packs	up to 50%	
Treatment Oils	For oily/large-pored skin	up to 40%	
Computer anti-radiation products	Creams	up to 15%	10-12%
Bath products	Bath Oils	up to 50%	
	To give homemade, cold process Soaps extra softness	20%	

Table 37: Percentages of Sunflower Oil to use in products

Sweet Almond Oil

Sweet Almond
INCI name: Prunus amygdalus dulcis

Description

A distinction is made between sweet (*Prunus amygdalus dulcis*) and bitter Almond (*Prunus amygdalus amara*), both of which produce oil. Sweet almonds contain approximately 45% oil; bitter almonds approximately 38% oil. Oil from bitter almonds goes rancid more easily, and is not suitable for use on skin as it may cause prussic acid poisoning. So, sweet almond oil is the best and certainly the safest one to use. Sweet almond oil is obtained from the seed of the almond tree, which grows up to 6-8 metres high and carries large quantities of beautiful white or red blossoms. The fruit contains a 'stone' with a hard shell around the seed. Sweet almond oil is a clear, light yellow oil with a pleasant taste and odour. It is much thinner and runnier than e.g. olive oil, consisting mainly of oleic acid and containing almost no solid fatty acids. A classic, mild, soft, smooth and semi-fatty oil, which spreads nicely and makes the skin soft, smooth and supple. It can be used for most skin types and in a variety of products. Very similar in properties to the other *Prunus* oils, namely apricot kernel oil, and peach kernel oil. Sweet almond oil is very light sensitive; direct sunlight makes it go rancid.

The SAP value for sweet almond oil is 136-137g.

Absorption Note

Middle.

Natural Vitamin Content

Approximately 0.03%, or 30mg per 100ml of sweet almond oil of vitamin E (naturally occurring d-alpha tocopherol).

Origin

Almond trees are grown in (amongst other places) the Mediterranean, Southwest Asia, China, Japan, California, Australia. The oil from Europe mainly comes from Italy and Spain.

Shelf Life

Keeps for 2-2.5 years.

Freezing Point

-18°C (-0.4°F).

Contraindications/warnings

Check for nut allergies with client.

Uses of Sweet Almond Oil

- Almond oil has been used since antiquity and is a classic oil for skin care.
- It is considered to be mild, non-irritating skin oil, which spreads well, is easily absorbed by the skin and makes it soft, smooth and supple.
- It has a semi-oily to oily feeling on the skin.
- Good for all skin types.
- It is a middle note vegetable oil.
- Can be used in massage oils, skin creams, ointments, etc.
- It's soft on the skin and is known as a long oil. This means that it can cover a large surface area with just one drop and spreads well. In contrast, short oils such as castor, evening primrose and shea butter do not spread well.
- It has a long 'surface time' which means that it is slowly absorbed by the skin and is therefore excellent for whole body massage oil.
- It blends well with all different types of vegetable oils.
- Oil-based perfumes (due to its lack of fragrance).
- In products for itchy skin.
- Excellent for baby products.
- Softens the skin and wound crusts.
- In eczema, psoriasis and acne creams.
- In make-up removers and in cleansing products (use up to 100%).
- In hair packs and oils.
- Not generally used for culinary purposes but makes a good salad dressing oil.
- These qualities refer to refined and cold pressed sweet almond oils. Cold pressed sweet almond oil, preferably organic, is the best quality.

Fatty Acid (Maximum) Content of Sweet Almond Oil

Please note, as the percentages in this illustration are for the maximum amount of fatty acid content found in sweet almond oil, they may add up to more than 100%.

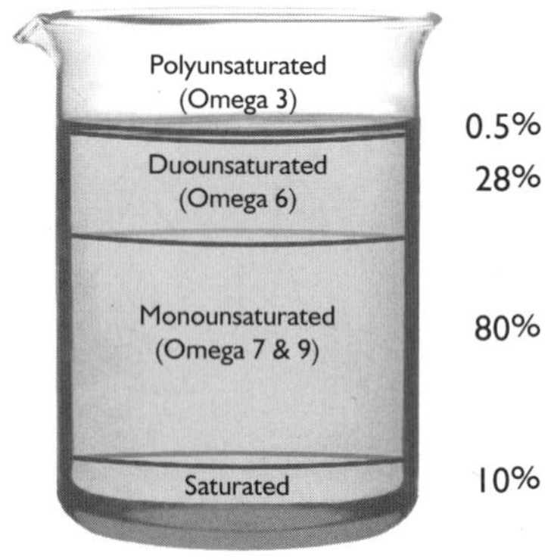

Breakdown of Fatty Acid content of Sweet Almond Oil	
Saturated	Palmitic Acid 6-8%
	Stearic Acid 0.5-2%
Mono-unsaturated	Oleic Acid 60-79%
	Palmitoleic Acid 0.4-0.7%
	Eicosenoic Acid <0.5%
Duo-unsaturated	Linoleic Acid 17-28%
Poly-unsaturated	Alpha Linolenic Acid 0.5%

Sweet Almond Oil Sample Recipes

The following Recipes make 100ml.

Swedish Massage Oil for dry or sensitive skin

35ml Sweet Almond Oil
35ml Apricot or Peach Kernel Oil
20ml Thistle Oil
7ml Hemp Seed Oil
3ml/g Vitamin E Oil (undiluted)

Swedish Massage Oil for dry skin Recipe 1

30ml Sweet Almond Oil
15ml Apricot or Peach Kernel Oil
15ml Coconut Oil (melt in bain-marie first, then add to the blend)
15ml Jojoba Oil
23ml Olive Oil
2ml/g Vitamin E Oil (undiluted)

Swedish Massage Oil for dry skin Recipe 2

95ml Sweet Almond Oil
5ml/g Vitamin E Oil (undiluted)
5 drops Rosemary Antioxidant (CO_2 Extract)

Anti-Wrinkle Cure Oil for dry skin Recipe

50ml Sweet Almond Oil
25ml Thistle Oil
10ml Apricot or Peach Kernel Oil
15ml/g Vitamin E Oil (undiluted)
5 drops Rosemary Antioxidant (CO_2 Extract)

Eye Make-up Remover

50ml Sweet Almond Oil
48ml Castor Oil
2ml Vitamin E Oil (undiluted)

Face Cure Oil for mature or sensitive skin

20ml Sweet Almond Oil
45ml Evening Primrose or Borage Oil
10ml Rosehip Oil
10ml Apricot or Peach Kernel Oil
5ml Thistle Oil
10ml Vitamin E Oil (undiluted)
5 drops Rosemary Antioxidant (CO_2 Extract)

Anti-Itching Treatment Oil

60ml Sweet Almond Oil
30ml Apricot or Peach Kernel Oil
5ml Castor Oil
4ml/g Vitamin E Oil (undiluted)
0.5g Menthol Crystals
20-25 drops Peppermint Essential Oil

NB Crush the Menthol Crystals into the Peppermint Oil and then add to your blend.

Skin Cleansing Oil

For all skin types. Apply with a cotton bud.
65ml Sweet Almond Oil
30ml Castor Oil
5ml/g Vitamin E Oil (undiluted)
5 drops Rosemary Antioxidant (CO_2 Extract)

Baby Oil for everyday use

40ml Sweet Almond Oil
30ml Apricot Oil
15ml Shea Butter Oil
13ml Rosehip Oil
2ml/g Vitamin E Oil (undiluted)

Percentages of Sweet Almond Oil to use in products

Product	Product details	How much Oil you can use in the product	Average use
Skin Rejuvenation/ Anti-Wrinkle products	Creams	up to 10%	5-6%
	Rejuvenating Body/Skin Oils	up to 50%	20-25%
Oils for all skin types	Face Oils/Serums	up to 20%	
Massage and Body Care products	Whole Body Massage Oil Blends for all skin types, except for oily/large-pored skin	up to 70%	
	Whole Body Massage Oil Blends for oily/large-pored skin	up to 40%	20-30%
	Massage Creams and Lotions	Up to 60% - use Emulsifan CB, which creates a water-in-fat emulsion.	45-55%
Anti-Itching products	Anti-itching Skin Oil	up to 60%	
Eczema and Psoriasis Treatment products	Treatment Creams	up to 15%	4-6%
	Treatment Oils	up to 40%	20-30%
Acne Treatment products	Treatment Creams	up to 8%	5-6%
	Treatment Oils	20%	10-15%
Perfumes	Oil-based Perfumes	up to 100%	
Hair Care products	Hair Oils and Packs	up to 50%	
Creams	Creams for all skin types, except for oily/large-pored skin	up to 15%	6-8%
Baby products	Baby Oils	up to 50%	
	Baby Creams for everyday use	up to 16%	8-10%
Cleansing products *Add Castor Oil to the Recipe for Cleansing products.*	Cleansing Oils	up to 70%	
	Cleansing Creams and Lotions	up to 50%	20-30%
Lip products	Lip Balms	Up to 100% of Vegetable Oil content of the Recipe.	

Table 38: Percentages of Sweet Almond Oil to use in products

Thistle Oil

Thistle

INCI name: Carthamus tinctorius

© ene. Image from BigStockPhoto.com

Description

Synonym: Safflower oil.

Thistle is an oil seed crop that is a member of the thistle (*Compositae*) family and produces its seed in heads. A dry to very dry, thin oil, which is refined or cold pressed from these seeds. An excellent source of omega 6 & 3 essential fatty acids (also known as vitamin F), as they can make up over 80% of the oil content. Thistle is particularly high in omega 6 (up to 81%). Of all the vegetable oils, thistle oil has, in fact, the highest content of linoleic acid, an omega 6 essential fatty acid. This makes it easy for the skin to absorb and it is a versatile oil that can be used in all kinds of skin care products due to the high vitamin F content.

The SAP value for thistle oil is 136-137g.

Absorption Note

Top.

Natural Vitamin Content

0.035-0.075%, or 35-75mg per 100ml of thistle oil of vitamin E (naturally occurring d-alpha tocopherol).

Origin

Native to the Mediterranean region but now also produced in Australia, USA, China, India, parts of Africa.

Shelf Life

2 years.

Freezing Point

-10 to -20°C (+14 to -4°F).

For more information

- See page 7 for 'More information on essential fatty acids (vitamin F)'.
- See page 15 for information on 'Rebalancing certain skin types with vegetable oils'.
- See page 29 for how to make an oil compress.

Uses of Thistle Oil

- Thistle oil has the highest content (up to 81%) of linoleic acid (omega 6) than any other vegetable oil.

Because organic thistle oil is relatively cheap and such a rich source of essential fatty acid, I personally think that you could put in a small quantity of organic thistle oil in every treatment oil blend, cream, lotion, massage oil and face oil that you make.

- The main quality of thistle oil is that it is nourishing for the skin and body.

- Thistle oil also helps to reduce the size of the pores. It is therefore excellent for people who want to rebalance their skin type from large-pored to normal skin.

- It is a top note vegetable oil, which means that it is absorbed very quickly by the skin.

- It blends well with other oils.

- Because it is very dry, and has a rough texture, don't use it on its own, but mix it with fattier and softer oils such as apricot kernel, peach kernel, sweet almond, avocado and macadamia nut oil, in massage and skin care products (especially for sensitive, mature and dry skin). The exception to this rule is when you are using thistle oil to increase circulation in the feet and legs.

- As thistle oil is a rough, half-long oil, always add long oils such jojoba oil, and softer oils such as peach kernel, apricot kernel, sweet almond, avocado or olive oil to thistle oil-based massage blends.

- Grape seed oil is a good alternative to thistle oil in massage oil blends for people with oily skin or skin with large pores.

- It has a rough feeling on the skin so for face oils blend with softer and smoother oils such as evening primrose, rosehip, coconut, macadamia nut, vitamin E and the *Prunus rosaceae* oils i.e. apricot kernel, peach kernel, and sweet almond.

- In eczema treatment products.

- In mature skin treatment products.

- Although suitable for all skin types, thistle oil is particularly good for use on oily, large-pored or acne-prone skin; or thin and sensitive or damaged skin that results from the topical use of cortisone treatments. Skin atrophy (which is from the Greek 'atrophia', meaning lack of nourishment) is a skin condition resulting from the use of corticosteroid creams/hydrocortisone products. Acute and extreme cases of skin atrophy can result in the thinning of the top two layers of skin, the dermis and epidermis, causing a depression in the skin. Thistle oil can improve the condition after a few weeks of applying it and the condition will usually disappear in a few months of applying the oil.

- The linoleic acid (omega 6) helps and relieves problems with poor blood circulation in feet and legs. This poor circulation can result in cramps, swollen feet or legs, discolouring, pain, leg ulcers, broken nails, etc.

- The enhanced circulation that results from the thistle oil pack treatment shows in a number of ways: the feet and legs will regain a normal temperature levels; discolouring and pain disappears; cold feet can become warm after just one night's oil pack (see recipes), itchiness after three days' oil application, leg ulcers and blemishes, as well as itching scars, can disappear or be much better after a week's treatment; pain can disappear after a month.

If you want to treat chapped skin at the same time, add 2% calendula CO_2 extract or 10-15% macerated calendula oil. If you have problems with sweaty feet, athlete's foot, or smelly feet, add 2-3% of tea tree essential oil plus 0.5% (10-12 drops per 100ml of recipe) of lavender essential oil. Don't use the oil pack every night but interchange it every other night with a warm foot bath containing rosemary, pine and juniper essential oils, which enhance circulation.

- Apply to finger- or toe- nails for increased circulation and nourishment. The oil treatments will help heal brittle nails that tend to split easily.

- After using thistle oil in products now for over 15 years, I have to say that only a tiny percentage of people have had a negative skin reaction to it.

- For culinary purposes, it has a mild, slightly nutty taste and has a light yellow colour. It is best used in salad dressings, as it is not good cooking oil due to the fact that cold pressed or unrefined thistle oil becomes altered when heated to high temperatures and has a very low smoke point of +109°C/+228°F. However, you can buy the refined oil that has no taste and smell and use that for cooking oil as that has a much higher smoke point of +263°C/+505°F.

Fatty Acid (Maximum) Content of Thistle Oil

Please note, as the percentages in the following illustration are for the maximum amount of fatty acid content found in thistle oil, they may add up to more than 100%.

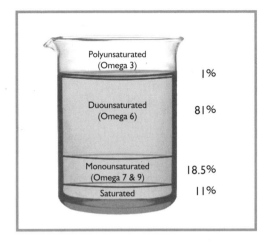

Breakdown of Fatty Acid content of Thistle Oil	
Saturated	Palmitic Acid 5-8%
	Stearic Acid 2-3%
Mono-unsaturated	Oleic Acid 12-18%
	Palmitoleic Acid <0.5%
Duo-unsaturated	Linoleic Acid 70-81%
Poly-unsaturated	Alpha Linolenic Acid <1%

Thistle Oil Sample Recipes

These Recipes make 100ml.

Treatment Oil for Stretch Marks

40ml Thistle Oil
10ml Evening Primrose Oil
50ml/g Vitamin E Oil (undiluted)
10 drops Rosemary Antioxidant (CO_2 Extract)

Rheumatism Treatment Oil

50ml Thistle Oil
40ml Rosehip Oil
10ml/g Vitamin E Oil (undiluted)
5 drops Rosemary Antioxidant (CO_2 Extract)

Face Oil/Serum for large-pored skin

50ml Thistle Oil
20ml Rosehip Oil
10ml Borage Oil
20ml/g Vitamin E Oil (undiluted)
5 drops Rosemary Antioxidant (CO_2 Extract)

Anti-Cellulite Oil

27ml Thistle Oil
27ml Borage Oil
27ml Rosehip Oil
19ml/g Vitamin E Oil (undiluted)
5 drops Rosemary Antioxidant (CO_2 Extract)

Swedish Massage Oil

40ml Thistle Oil
40ml Sweet Almond Oil
15ml Jojoba Oil
5ml/g Vitamin E Oil (undiluted)
5 drops Rosemary Antioxidant (CO_2 Extract)

Itchy Skin Treatment Oil

40ml Thistle Oil
30ml Apricot Kernel Oil
10ml St. John's Wort Oil
19ml/g Vitamin E Oil (undiluted)
1ml/g Chamomile CO_2 Extract
5 drops Rosemary Antioxidant (CO_2 Extract)

Warming Massage Oil

30ml Thistle Oil
30ml Rosehip Oil
30ml Castor Oil
10ml/g Vitamin E Oil (undiluted)
5 drops Rosemary Antioxidant (CO_2 Extract)

Brittle Nail Treatment Oil

40ml Thistle Oil
25ml Sesame Oil
10ml Comfrey Oil
10ml Pumpkin Seed Oil (for its high zinc content)
15ml/g Vitamin E Oil (undiluted)
5 drops Rosemary Antioxidant (CO_2 Extract)

Circulation Boost Skin Oil for legs and feet

50ml Thistle Oil
20ml Jojoba Oil
20ml Evening Primrose Oil
10ml/g Vitamin E Oil (undiluted)
5 drops Rosemary Antioxidant (CO_2 Extract)

Thistle Oil Pack for circulation and warmer feet

80ml Thistle Oil
10ml Castor Oil
10ml/g Vitamin E Oil (undiluted)

Method

1) Soak two cotton socks in a bowl of oil shown in the recipe above or in the 'Circulation Boost Skin Oil for legs and feet' and 'Thistle Oil Pack for circulation and warmer feet'.

2) Squeeze a little of the oil out of the socks so that they are not dripping.

3) Put the socks on your feet and cover both feet with plastic bags.

4) Finally, cover the plastic bags with larger, dry socks.

5) Keep on overnight and remove in morning.

6) Repeat every other night, alternating with a warm foot bath containing essential oils that increase circulation (see 'Uses').

Percentages of Thistle Oil to use in products

Product	Product details	How much Oil you can use in the product	Average use
Massage products *Reminder: mix with 'long' and fatty Oils for massage purposes.*	Oil Blends for all skin types	up to 40%	10-15%
Body Oils	Oil Blends for oily or large-pored skin	up to 50%	20-30%
	Oil Blends for dry, mature skin	up to 30%	15-20%
Creams and Lotions	Creams for oily/large-pored skin	Note: A maximum of 15% total of Vegetable Oils are used in Cream Recipes for oily skin.	2-6%
	Creams for all other skin types	up to 12%	2-12%
	Lotions for all skin types	up to 6%	3-5%.
Skin Rejuvenation/ Anti-Wrinkle products	Face Oils/Serums	up to 30%	
Everyday Face Oils/ Serums	For all skin types.	Up to 50% - always mix with softer and smoother Oils for Face Oils.	
Eczema and Psoriasis Treatment products	Treatment Creams	up to 15%	2-6%
	Treatment Oils	up to 30%	
Acne Treatment products	Treatment Oils	Up to 20% - remember to always mix it with softer, smoother Oils e.g. Rosehip, Evening Primrose, Kiwi Seed.	
Nail Treatment products	Treatment Oils	up to 40%	
Circulation Enhancement products	Treatment Oils for circulation problems in the legs and feet	up to 60%	
	Foot Circulation Oil Packs	up to 100%	

/contd

186

contd/

Product	Product details	How much Oil you can use in the product	Average use
Post-Cortisone use products	Nourishing Skin Oils	Up to 40% - always add Vitamin- and GLA-rich Oils to the Blend.	
Body Butters, Balms and Ointments		up to 25%	
Elderly/sagging skin Treatment products	Treatment Creams	up to 12%	8-10%
	Treatment Oils	up to 40%	30-40%
Skin Rebalancing products	Treatment Oils to rebalance skin type from oily/large-pored to more normal skin	Up to 50% - mix it with e.g. Rosehip or Camelina Oils or Squalane.	

Table 39: Percentages of Thistle to use in products

Walnut Oil

Walnut
INCI name: Juglans regia

Description

The oil is cold pressed from the nuts, which contain 50-60% oil and are stored before pressing. The cold pressed oil has a nutty taste and is yellow in colour.

Walnut oil is widely used for culinary purposes, in cooking and in salad dressings and in baking speciality bread. Walnut oil is rich (11-14%) in omega 3 essential fatty acid (alpha linolenic acid). It is a dry oil, easily absorbed by the skin and is excellent for skin regeneration products for mature skin.

The SAP value for walnut oil is 135-136g.

Absorption Note

Top.

Natural Vitamin Content

0.05%, or 50mg per 100ml of walnut oil of vitamin E (naturally occurring d-alpha tocopherol).

Origin

Native to the Himalayan region, China and eastern Europe. Nowadays the USA and France are large producers of walnut. The trees are grown for their timber and edible nuts.

Shelf Life

Keeps for 1.5-2 years.

Freezing Point

0°C (+32°F).

Contraindications/warnings

Check for nut allergies with client.

Further information

- Walnut oil is easily absorbed by the skin because of its high content of linoleic acid (up to 65%).
- Walnut oil has less linoleic acid (an omega 6 fatty acid) than thistle oil, but about the same as good quality cold pressed sunflower oil. However, walnut oil has a relatively high content (up to 14%) of alpha linolenic acid (an omega 3 fatty acid), whereas thistle has a very low omega 3 content. So, the total

content of omega 3 and omega 6 fatty acids (collectively called vitamin F) is equivalent to thistle oil and walnut and thistle oils complement each other well.

- See page 7 for 'More information about essential fatty acids (vitamin F).

- See page 29 for how to make an oil compress.

Uses of Walnut Oil

- Walnut oil has a high content of omega 3 essential fatty acids (up to 14%). At the time of writing this book walnut oil is a cost-effective source of omega 3, compared with most other omega 3-rich oils.

- Walnut oil has a dry feeling on the skin and disperses well on the skin, leaving the skin soft and supple.

- It works well for oily and large-pored skin and skin and is especially good for general regeneration of the skin, which makes it perfect for anti-wrinkle blends and blends for mature and over-40s skin.

- As the oil is dry and it is absorbed quickly by the skin, it doesn't work very well when used on its own for whole body massage. Blend it with fattier and longer oils in your massage oils. It is not sticky and offers resistance, which is good for classic massage use. For aromatherapy purposes, you can blend it with longer and softer oils such as avocado, sweet almond, apricot kernel, peach kernel, or olive.

- Use it as a skin, nail or body oil where you want to increase circulation i.e. legs and feet, on leg ulcers, discoloured skin, brittle nails, etc.

- In eczema treatment products.

- In products that treat different types of itchy skin.

- In acne treatment products.

- In hair products that treat scalp problems such as itchy scalp or dandruff.

- Helps to heal superficial burns and sunburn. Blend with vitamin E oil and St. John's wort oil for after-sun oil blends. It is said to protect the skin from UV rays.

- When using walnut oil in your cream recipes, don't add too much of it as the walnutty smell may dominate the cream.

Fatty Acid (Maximum) Content of Walnut Oil

Please note, as the percentages below are for the maximum amount of fatty acid content found in walnut oil, they may add up to more than 100%.

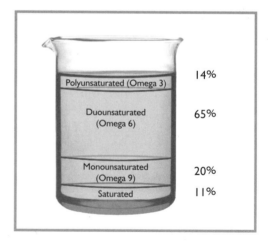

Polyunsaturated (Omega 3)	14%
Duounsaturated (Omega 6)	65%
Monounsaturated (Omega 9)	20%
Saturated	11%

Breakdown of Fatty Acid content of Walnut Oil	
Saturated	Palmitic Acid 6-8%
	Stearic Acid 2-3%
Mono-unsaturated	Oleic Acid 16-20%

Duo-unsaturated	Linoleic Acid 50-65%
Poly-unsaturated	Alpha Linolenic Acid 11-14%

Walnut Oil Sample Recipes

These Recipes make 100ml. **NB** The blends will smell quite strongly of walnut.

Body Oil for mature or sensitive skin

30ml Walnut Oil
30ml Jojoba Oil
25ml Macadamia Nut Oil
10ml Borage Oil
5ml/g Vitamin E Oil (undiluted)
5 drops Rosemary Antioxidant (CO_2 Extract)

Everyday Acne Treatment Oil

For everyday use.
40ml Walnut Oil
40ml Borage Oil
10ml Jojoba Oil
9ml/g Vitamin E Oil (undiluted)
1ml/g Vitamin A Palmitate
5 drops Rosemary Antioxidant (CO_2 Extract)

Simple Anti-Wrinkle Oil/Serum

40ml Walnut Oil
40ml Rosehip Oil
20ml/g Vitamin E Oil (undiluted)
5 drops Rosemary Antioxidant (CO_2 Extract)

Anti-Wrinkle Oil/Serum for mature skin

40ml Walnut Oil
20ml Thistle Oil
10ml Macadamia Nut Oil
8ml Evening Primrose Oil
5ml Pumpkin Seed Oil
15ml/g Vitamin E Oil (undiluted)
1ml Echium CO_2 Extract
1ml Arctic Blackcurrant Seed CO_2 Extract
5 drops Rosemary Antioxidant (CO_2 Extract)

Warming Leg Oil for increasing circulation

70ml Walnut Oil
10ml Castor Oil
10ml Sunflower Oil
10ml/g Vitamin E Oil (undiluted)
5 drops Rosemary Antioxidant (CO_2 Extract)

Itchy Scalp Treatment Oil

Apply and massage in 2-3 times a week. Leave on for 1-2 hours and then wash hair with a mild shampoo. **NB** *Apply shampoo to the hair, before rinsing with water - this will help remove the Oil.*
60ml Walnut Oil
22ml Apricot Kernel Oil
10ml St. John's Wort Oil
5ml/g Vitamin E Oil (undiluted)
2ml/g Chamomile CO2 Extract
1ml/g Vitamin A Palmitate
5 drops Rosemary Antioxidant (CO_2 Extract)

Percentages of Walnut Oil to use in products

Product	Product details	How much Oil you can use in the product	Average use
Massage products	Swedish Massage Oil Blends	up to 25%	
	Oil Blends for oily/large-pored skin	up to 30%	
	Massage Blends that increase blood circulation	up to 30%	
Skin Rejuvenation/ Anti-Wrinkle products	Face Oils/Serums for dry, mature skin	up to 40%	
	Body/Skin Oils	up to 30%	
	Creams for oily skin	up to 7%	4-5%
	Creams for dry, mature skin	up to 15%	6-8%
Scalp Treatment problems	Dandruff Treatment Oils	up to 40%	
	Anti-Itch scalp Treatment Oils	Up to 60% - combine with 40% St. John's Wort Oil.	
Eczema Treatment products	Treatment Creams	up to 15%	6-8%
	Treatment Oils	up to 25%	
Acne Treatment products	Treatment Creams	up to 15%	8-10%
	Everyday Acne Treatment Oils	up to 50%	
Circulation Treatment products	Treatment Oils for circulation problems in the legs and feet	up to 70%	
Lifting products for elderly/sagging skin	Lifting Creams	up to 10%	6-8%
	Lifting Oils	up to 20%	10-15%
Nail Care products	Nail Care Oils	Up to 40%	
Sun Protection and Care products	After Sun Oil Blend	Up to 30% - remember to blend with Vitamin E Oil and St. John's Wort Oil.	

Table 40: Percentages of Walnut Oil to use in products

Bibliography &
References

Bibliography

Borseth, Kolbjørn, The Aromantic Guide to making your own Natural Skin, Hair and Body Care products, 2007. ISBN 978-0-9554323-1-6.

Borseth, Kolbjørn, The Aromantic Guide to the use of Herbs in Skin, Hair and Health Care products, 2006. ISBN 978-0-9554323-0-9.

Andersen, Finn, *Guldet från växterna, Kristianstad boktryckeri*, 2004. ISBN 91-974063-7-6

Price, Len; Smith, Ian; Price, Shirley, Carrier oils for aromatherapy & massage, Riverhead, 2004. ISBN 1 874353 02 6

www.wikipedia.org.uk

www.shenet.se

References

1) Archives of Dermatological Research, pages 375-381, July 1998.

2) Clinical and Experimental Dermatology, pages 56-58, March 1998.

3) Journal of Investigative Dermatology, pages 1096-1101, May 1996.

4) Seminars in Dermatology, pages 169-175, June 1992.

5) "Plant oils: Topical application and anti-inflammatory effects (croton oil test)". Dermatol. Monatsschr, page 179, 1993.

6) "Digital image analysis of the effect of topically applied linoleic acid on acne microcomedones". Clinical & Experimental Dermatology 23 (2): pages 56-58. PMID: 9692305, March 1998.

7) "Impact of topical oils on the skin barrier: possible implications for neonatal health in developing countries". Acta Paediatrica 91 (5): pages 546-55, 2002.

hamlyn

Leonardo DiCaprio

THE ILLUSTRATED STORY

CAROLINE WESTBROOK

The author would like to thank the following for their assistance and support: Julian Brown, Leslie Bunder, Karen O'Grady, Pamela Melnikoff, Helen and David Westbrook, Ian and Marsha Westbrook, Hugh Westbrook and Melissa Green, UUNET UK, AOL UK, (http://www.carrera.co.uk). And last but by no means least, a special big thank you to Good Ghost (we still have imaginary friends!. . .)

Executive Editor Julian Brown
Editor Karen O'Grady and Tarda Davison-Aitkins
Design Richard Scott and Geoff Fennell
Picture Research Maria Gibbs and Zoe Holtermann
Production Mark Walker and Sarah Scanlan

CONTENTS

First published in Great Britain in 1997
by Hamlyn,an imprint of Octopus Publishing Group
2–4 Heron Quays
London E14 4JP

Copyright © 1999 Octopus Publishing Group

Reprinted 1998
Revised and updated in 1999

ISBN 0 600 59883 7

A catalogue record for this book is available from the British Library

Printed by Cayfosa in Spain

1

Kicking and Screaming

UNIVERSAL STUDIOS.
PRODUCER
DIRECTOR

SCENE	TAKE	ROLL

DATE	PROD. NO.

From the Hollywood slums to the sitcom world, Leonardo's upbringing was far from conventional

Leonardo DiCaprio was born to be a star. At the age of only 25, this blond Californian is seemingly loved by absolutely everybody, from a globe-wide body of fans, who cherish his boyish good looks and astounding acting talent, to the critics who just can't praise him enough. Not for nothing has DiCaprio been pronounced the best new actor of his generation. His performances in the likes of *What's Eating Gilbert Grape?* (For which he was Oscar-nominated), and the more recent *William Shakespeare's Romeo And Juliet* prove that he really is more than just a pretty face – he is a captivating screen presence. And yet somehow he still manages not to sell out – by choosing interesting roles over potential box office money spinners he has won himself an enormous degree of respect with everybody who sees his work.

In fact, there's something altogether different about Leonardo DiCaprio – while a lot of his peers appear introverted and prefer to shun the limelight, Leonardo takes it all in his stride, and despite playing a string of intense, tortured young men onscreen, is described as a lively hyperactive figure behind the camera, who spends most of his time joking around with his co-stars and is happiest living a comparatively normal existence away from the cameras. 'I think it has to do with me not investing everything in my job,' he said in a recent interview. 'All these actors think that the blood through their veins is fuelled by acting, but I'm happier hanging out with my friends when I'm not working.' If world domination is just a step away, he is clearly making no attempt to avoid it. Such an attitude probably stems from what can only be described as an unconventional childhood.

Leonardo Wilhelm DiCaprio was born on November 11, 1974 in Los Angeles, California, the only child of German mother Irmelin (none too surprisingly, Leonardo speaks fluent German) and Italian father George. He also has a stepbrother, Adam. His striking first name came about during a trip that his mother made to Italy's Uffizi Gallery while she was pregnant; while admiring a Leonardo Da Vinci painting, her unborn son decided to pitch in with a swift kick, something she interpreted as a message telling her what to name the child.

Although he was brought up just a stone's throw from Tinseltown, Leonardo's early life was far from glamorous. Living in what he later described as the slums of Hollywood, his hippy parents had split up before he had even blown out the candles on his first birthday cake, although they never divorced and remain close friends to this day, working together on managing their son's career (his mother concentrates on the financial side of things, while his dad surveys the dozens of scripts that come crashing through the letter box every week). Their son, likewise, is equally close to his parents, so much so that he only moved out of his mother's house last year.

However, Leonardo's upbringing was also a bohemian one that proved to be enormously

Above: *Parenthood:* Gil (Ed Begley Jr. takes on nephew Jerry (Leonardo) in the annual backyard basketball championships

Smash sit-com *Roseanne* provided Leonardo with one of his many TV appearances

Above: Leonardo joined forces with the world's most famous collie in *The New Lassie* – but only for two episodes

Opposite: Leonardo as he appeared in *Growing Pains*, playing homeless teen Luke Brower

influential on his later life: his dad ran a business from his garage, producing underground comic books and comic arts, while his mother quit her more conventional job as a legal secretary to manage Leonardo's acting career when it began to take off. Throughout Leonardo's childhood, the house would be full of high profile visitors, including writers such as Charles Bukowski and fellow underground satirical comic artist Robert Crumb.

From an early age, Leonardo was restless and hyperactive, especially in the classroom, and at both his schools, the Center For Enriched Studies and John Marshall High School, he got more of a kick out of being the class clown, and providing lunchtime entertainments in the playground for his friends, than battening down to his studies. He often cheated in lessons (especially maths) and skipped homework altogether. 'I was always known as the crazy little kid,' he says, 'and I never got the knack of school. I could never focus on things I didn't want to learn. Instead I used to take half the school and do break-dancing skits with my friends in front of them at lunchtime.'

But he had already found a way in which to channel his energies. Long before starting school, acting – of a sort – had beckoned, and when Leonardo was three, he made his debut on *Romper Room,* a long-running educational show for children beamed across the TV sets of America at an impossibly early hour. Even then, he seemed incapable of settling down, and before long he was unceremoniously removed from the set due to his unruly behaviour. It was his last appearance in front of a camera for nine years.

During this time, Leonardo was blazing the audition trail, with comparatively little success; and at the age of ten he nearly quit the business altogether after one agent suggested, none too tactfully, that he alter his 'wrong' haircut and change his name to the far less foreign sounding Lenny Williams. It was incidents such as these which left Leonardo disillusioned with the commercialism of the industry he was trying to break into. But with his parents encouragement, and the added incentive of his stepbrother's appearance on a hugely successful commercial for Golden Grahams cereal, he kept going, and finally landed himself an agent at the age of 14.

Leonardo's initial work was in television, appearing in over 30 commercials, and educational films with such titles as *Mickey's Safety Club* and *How To Deal With A Parent Who Takes Drugs*. When he was 15, he also had a part of the blink-and-you'll-miss-it variety in the TV series of *Parenthood*, the spin-off show from Ron Howard's hugely successful 1990 film, which starred Steve Martin as the neurotic head of an ever-expanding family, and also featured a very young looking Keanu Reeves as his niece's race car-fixated boyfriend. But it wasn't long before the TV series began to pour in, and he made guest appearances on a whole range of popular programmes, including the soap opera *Santa Barbara*, sitcom smash *Roseanne* and *The Outsiders*, a TV spin-off series from the 1983 hit film of the same name. Also on the agenda were two episodes of *The New Lassie*, But Leonardo did not have to share centre stage with a heroic collie dog for long. At the age of 16, he landed his first regular TV role, on the hit series *Growing Pains*.

The show, a long-running success in the States which strangely failed to make it across the pond, was a sitcom aimed at teens, and extremely popular due to its handsome star, Kirk Cameron, who played Seavers, a well-meaning teen coping with the tribulations of adolescence. Leonardo appeared on the scene in 1990 and stayed for two series (24 episodes), starring as a streetwise homeless kid whom Cameron's character took pity on and invited into his home. Although it did wonders for DiCaprio's career and thrust him into the public eye more than anything he had done previously, the experience is not one he looks back on fondly. 'I couldn't bear it,' he has since said 'everybody was bright and chipper. But I got to know what I didn't want to do.'

Whatever Leonardo's opinions may have been of the show, the one thing it did prove to the hordes of viewers who tuned in every week was that he showed a good deal more potential than his co-stars. And while Kirk Cameron disappeared into relative obscurity once *Growing Pains* finally wound down, the co-star who had inadvertently stolen the limelight from his leading man went on to focus his attention fully on his greatest ambition – getting into the movies.

Leonardo takes a well-earned break from starring in sit-coms

Leonardo makes his debut with Kirk Cameron (right) on *Growing Pains* as Luke, the homeless teen accused of pilfering Jason's (Alan Thickie, left) wine collection

Not that Leonardo hadn't already shown his face in the multiplexes. In 1991, while still on the show, he took on his first starring role in a movie – that of Josh in cheapie horror sequel *Critters 3*. The latest in a franchise that had been marginally successful in the 1980's thanks to its release soon after the smash hit *Gremlins*, the series concentrates on a group of alien furballs invading earth and causing all manner of havoc – in this case, imprisoning the residents of a tower block in a plot not entirely dissimilar to disaster classic *The Towering Inferno*.

It's not the first time that a household name has turned to low-budget horror to make their mark on the movies – Brad Pitt's debut was in the equally forgettable slasher spoof *Cutting Class,* while *Friends'* star Jennifer Aniston was the love interest of a decidedly anti-social green monster in *Leprechaun* – but nonetheless, for obvious reasons, *Critters 3* does not figure too highly on the DiCaprio CV.

A much better choice for Leonardo turned out to be a small role in the teen psycho-thriller *Poison Ivy,* a film notable for marking the comeback of actress Drew Barrymore. As fellow student Guy, DiCaprio provided moral support to *Roseanne* star Sara Gilbert, who stars as Sylvie, an awkward loner befriending the beautiful new girl in class (Barrymore), only to discover that her new best pal has a major crush on her father and will stop at nothing (including murder) to get what she wants.

Poison Ivy was an enjoyable, tense thriller which didn't exactly register with cinema audiences but has since made its mark on video, although admittedly Leonardo was somewhat overshadowed by the superb performances from the two female leads.

But with his film career beginning to take off nicely, it would only be a matter of time before he did leave an impression of his own, and he did it by starring with none other than Robert De Niro.

2

This Boy's Break

Leonardo's move into movies grabs a wealth of attention

Few actors can boast that they have appeared on screen alongside Robert de Niro before they reach their 18th birthday, while even fewer could be said to have out-acted the man himself. However, Leonardo DiCaprio not only has the former credit on his ever-expanding list of roles, but was regarded by many to have achieved the latter at the same time – giving him the 'big break' he had been waiting for since the age of five. It's all thanks to a little-known movie called *This Boy's Life,* which may have made a swift exit from cinemas but had more impact on Leonardo's career than he could ever have dreamed of.

This Boy's Life gave Leonardo his big break in movies

This Boy's Life: Leonardo as Toby, attempts to bond with stepfather Dwight (Robert De Niro)

Set in the 1950's, and based on a true story by writer Tobias Wolff, *This Boy's Life* is a grim, but compelling coming-of-age tale directed by British filmmaker Michael Caton-Jones (who also shouted the orders on World War II drama *Memphis Belle* and Scottish epic *Rob Roy*). Ellen Barkin (*Sea Of Love*, *The Fan*) is Caroline Wolff, single parent to three boys, including eldest son Toby (DiCaprio), living in smalltown America, and being taunted by an abusive boyfriend.

In order to escape the regular beatings, Barkin and son flee to begin a new life in the dour, grey town of Concrete, Washington, where she meets and rapidly marries a local mechanic, Dwight (De Niro), not stopping to think of the possible consequences.

He, however, turns out to be an alcoholic every bit as abusive as the man they have escaped, taking an instant dislike to his new stepson in the process, and when the domestic violence begins again Toby takes the brunt of his new parent's abuse: Dwight steals the money from his paper round and refuses to buy him basketball shoes so that he is forced to play barefoot.

None too surprisingly, Toby begins hanging around with the wrong crowd and getting a reputation in the neighbourhood for being troublesome, although in-between there's also time for a spot of teen romance and a touching relationship with his openly gay best friend. (Jonah Blechman). When his mother proves to be resigned to her husband's tendencies, it is down to Toby to convince her to flee Concrete and set up home elsewhere. Only then can mother and sons renew their bonds.

This particular role proved an extraordinary challenge from the start, with Leonardo beating 400 other young actors to land the part of Tobias Wolff, and quitting his regular role on *Growing Pains* to make the movie. Then there was the task of working with Robert De Niro, often lauded as the finest actor of his generation. A daunting prospect certainly – initially an actor as renowned as De Niro would seem unapproachable – but despite their onscreen hatred for one another, the pair hit it off tremendously once the cameras were switched off, DiCaprio's reputation for being laid-back and easy-going on sets coming to the fore. DiCaprio has since said

that he cherished the whole experience, crediting De Niro for his support and encouragement, and for providing him with vital acting advice as the shoot progressed, which has proved an invaluable boost to his on-screen offerings ever since. It comes as no surprise that, along with Jack Nicholson and Meg Ryan, he lists De Niro as one of his favourite screen stars.

Sadly, it was a dynamite combination which did little to boost the public interest. *This Boy's Life* was released in the US on April 23, 1993 – traditionally a quiet period at the US box office prior to the release of the all-conquering summer blockbuster season which would that year include the biggest film of all time *Jurassic Park*. The Spring release should, by rights, have given the movie a fighting chance, but the film disappeared from American cinemas after only a fortnight when the takings proved to be hugely disappointing – so much so, that *This Boy's Life* only secured a British release the following summer, and was given an extremely minor cinema outing before being sent swiftly to video. However, the small screen proved to be its saving grace, for the film received a much wider audience there than it had previously done at the pictures. If anything deterred prospective audiences, though, it must have been that the story was too depressing and moody for the thrill-seeking Saturday night crowds, because the film proved a smash hit with critics, many of whom rated *This Boy's Life* as one of the best films of the year. While Robert De Niro's performance received the inevitable plaudits, it was notable that the majority of the praise rested on the shoulders of his young co-star, many suggesting that his likeable, natural performance had completely stolen the show from the film's legendary lead.

Leonardo was praised by many reviewers for his outstanding performance as troubled teenager Toby. Such influential papers as the *Chicago Sun-Times* (with a write-up penned by hugely famous film critic Roger Ebert) and the *Washington Post* could not heap enough praise on Leonardo and the phrase 'the next big thing' began to be bandied about quite comfortably, while others lamented the fact that Tobias Wolff had not lived long enough to see himself portrayed so effectively onscreen.

Even trade bible *Variety* got in on the act, saying 'Centrescreen almost throughout, DiCaprio is excellent as Toby.'

When it finally made its appearance in the UK, to equally enthusiastic reviews, the attention was once again focused on Leonardo. Elsewhere, teenage magazines were giving the film the sort of coverage it could never have hoped for had it not been for the presence of its handsome young star. And DiCaprio was not forgotten when awards time came around, either. While the Oscar nomination remained unforthcoming, a trio of trophies came his way from the various groups of movie critics across America who give their own awards out every year.

For his performances in both *This Boy's Life*, and that of *What's Eating Gilbert Grape?*, Leonardo became the proud recipient of the New Generation Award from the Los Angeles Film Critics Association, the Chicago Film Critics honoured him with their Most Promising Actor accolade, and to top it all off nicely, a Best Supporting Actor runners-up prize came his way from both the New York Film Critics and the National Society of Film Critics. Leonardo DiCaprio had, in a very real sense, arrived.

Leonardo and Robert De Niro were to be reunited at a later date in the film *Marvin's Room*, the 1996 Oscar-nominated drama which received similar critical plaudits but made an equally lukewarm impact at the box office. But while *This Boy's Life* may have been dismissed as one of the many casualties that litter the cinemas every week, for Leonardo this particular effort was no flash in the pan.

The teen who once admitted that he wanted to be an actor because it would be a cool way for all the girls to notice him was getting attention for more than just his good looks. But while he could have taken the route of so many of his peers and chosen a more high-profile, handsome leading man role, his next outing proved to be a serious case of casting against type, a role which, like so many he has chosen since, gave his amazing acting talents a chance to shine through in full. The film in question was the highly original *What's Eating Gilbert Grape?*, and Oscar nomination was just a matter of months away.

Leonardo in reflective mode in *This Boy's Life* (above) and, opposite, in one of the films lighter moments

Grape Expectations

Leonardo takes on his most challenging role to date in *What's Eating Gilbert Grape?* – and is justly rewarded for his efforts

In choosing *What's Eating Gilbert Grape?* as his follow-up to *This Boy's Life*, Leonardo showed himself to be an actor who refused to be pigeonholed into heart-throb roles, choosing interesting films over surefire hits. It is a trait that he shared with his Gilbert Grape co-star, Johnny Depp, who had by this time made a name for himself in a string of arthouse and off-the-wall projects (*Benny And Joon*, *Arizona Dream* to name but two), most of which had garnered him ecstatic reviews but, with the exception of *Edward Scissorhands*, had gone virtually unnoticed by the cinema-going public.

What's Eating Gilbert Grape? – the film that landed Leonardo a Best Supporting Actor nomination at the Oscars

What's Eating Gilbert Grape? is a quirky, often hilarious, and ultimately moving screen version of Peter Hedges' best-seller, directed by Swedish helmer Lasse Halstrom (previously best known for the 1970's classic *ABBA The Movie*). Johnny Depp stars as the title character, struggling to keep his head in a tiny town where everybody knows everybody else, and his dysfunctional family are somewhat infamous. Mom (Darlene Cates, who took up acting after being spotted on a talk show about agoraphobia) has ballooned to forty stone ever since their father hanged himself in the cellar, and is housebound; older sister Amy (Mary Kate Schellhardt) is put-upon, and duty bound to keep the family home together, and younger sister Ellen (Laura Harrington) is in the throes of adolescence and taking every teenage tantrum out on her unfortunate older brother.

DiCaprio, meanwhile, completes the family as Arnie, Gilbert's mentally handicapped sibling, who doctors said would not live to see the other side of ten. They were wrong. As the film opens, preparations are being made for Arnie's 18th birthday. While playful and well-meaning, Arnie's condition makes him highly uncontrollable; at one point he is arrested for climbing all the way to the top of the local TV tower, and baths become a thing of the past when he is accidentally left sitting in the tub all

night. And when Gilbert is trying to impress visitor Becky (Juliette Lewis), by giving her a lift back to her caravan, Arnie, ever aware of his own impending death, attempts to make friends with the new arrival by informing her that 'I could go at any time . . .'

Although Leonardo did not have nearly such stiff competition when it came to the role of Arnie Grape as he had for that of Tobias Wolff, there were still obstacles to overcome, the main one being when he nearly lost out on the part altogether because he was considered by many to be far too handsome to play something which was so unglamorous. Fortunately, his looks proved not to be his downfall, and prior to filming he researched the role thoroughly by spending a great deal of time with other mentally handicapped people, in order to gain inspiration for Arnie's on-screen shenanigans.

The film itself was almost impossible to fault, with superb performances all round, but once again it was Leonardo's which really stood out, his research having paid off greatly. While Arnie was prone to the sort of behaviour that only a saint could fail to find fault with, Leonardo proved so affecting and vulnerable in the role that it proved impossible not to love him, no matter what he got up to. He was almost a little too convincing, as it happens; many viewers unfamiliar with Leonardo were

Leonardo, as the handicapped Arnie Grape visits the grave of his long-dead father

A Grape bonding session, in one of the films more poignant scenes

so taken in by his acting that they believed the part was being played by a genuinely handicapped teenager.

Like *This Boy's Life*, though, *Gilbert Grape* was similarly overlooked when it came to ticket sales. Released in the winter of 1993, some eight months after the former had made its quiet debut, critics couldn't praise the movie highly enough, and Leonardo once again found himself on the receiving end of plaudits a-plenty, (in one particularly memorable incident, screenwriter William Goldman declared 'Please don't let anything bad ever happen to Leonardo DiCaprio') but this time around there was a blockbuster season to contend with, and the spectacle of Robin Williams donning the latex to play Scottish nanny *Mrs. Doubtfire* was far more of a draw for the majority of moviegoers.

Still, *Gilbert Grape's* Christmas cinema outing did have one notable advantage attached to it; that of the impending awards season. Traditionally, the movies most likely to be noticed when it comes to Oscar nomina-

tions are released right at the end of the year, in order for them to be fresh in the memories of the voters, and *Gilbert Grape* proved to be no exception. Although the film was not quite strong enough to be featured in the Best Picture category (in a year which saw the likes of *Schindler's List* and *The Piano* going home laden down with new silverware), Leonardo's superb presence had captured the imagination of award-givers everywhere. In addition to the joint rewards critics had heaped upon him for both *This Boy's Life* and *Gilbert Grape* (see Chapter 2), he also copped a Golden Globe Nomination for Best Supporting Actor for the latter, and found himself attending his first major awards ceremony.

Leonardo may have gone home empty-handed, but there were greater things to come. The Golden Globes is always seen as an accurate pointer as to who will be short-listed come Oscar night, and sure enough, when the Academy Award nominations were announced, Leonardo found his name up there for his superb performance in *What's*

Eating Gilbert Grape?, sharing the list with such luminaries as Tommy Lee Jones (*The Fugitive*), Ben Kingsley (*Schindler's List*), Ralph Fiennes (*Schindler's List*) and Pete Postlethwaite (*In The Name Of The Father*). It was a memorable Oscar year – the year that Stephen Spielberg finally broke his Oscar duck, and youngest ever Oscar winner Anna Paquin (Best Supporting Actress for *The Piano*) stood on the stage speechless in front of a viewing audience of millions. And judging by the enormous cheer that went up in the auditorium when his name was read out, Leonardo was one of the most popular nominees of the night. However, the competition proved just too stiff, and he eventually lost out to Tommy Lee Jones for his performance as the cop chasing Harrison Ford in *The Fugitive*.

The fact that he had achieved all this by the age of 19, however, proved that Leonardo was turning into a force to be reckoned with, something which became apparent when *Gilbert Grape* was released elsewhere in the world and gained some much deserved success. Although his name was still not one of those which could open a film, he was reaching the stage where he could be picky about what he starred in, and so he did just that.

The local wild life leaves Arnie Grape completely undaunted

Left: Gilbert Grape's on screen family: L–R, Leonardo, Laura Harrington, Johnny Depp, Darlene Cates, and Mary Kate Schellhardt

Leonardo finds a sympathetic shoulder in onscreen brother Gilbert Grape (Johnny Depp)

While many stars would take the choice of the plum roles offered to them, Leonardo kept his artistic integrity intact and turned down a whole string of high-profile parts that would have made him a household name.

First up was *Hocus Pocus*, Disney's comedy about three witches (headed by Bette Midler) burned at the stake and returning to inflict their revenge on Halloween, only to be seen off by a kid far brainier than they. The role would not only have made Leonardo a good deal wealthier, but would also have provided him with that as yet elusive box office hit; *Hocus Pocus* eventually went ahead with ex-*Dallas* star Omri Katz taking the lead, and made a modest if unspectacular amount of money.

Far more lucrative, though, was the opportunity to play Robin in *Batman Forever*, the third part in the phenomenally successful franchise concentrating on the 90's adventures of the Caped Crusader. Again, Leonardo turned down the part which eventually went to Chris O'Donnell, and unsurprisingly, the film

went on to be the biggest grosser of 1995. O'Donnell, meanwhile, found himself rocketing into the megastar league and was so popular that he once again donned tights and mask for 1997's summer offering, *Batman And Robin*, together with George Clooney, the third actor to play the caped crimefighter in the series. Had Leonardo opted for the part, it would have seen him carrying the character into the next millennium (a fifth Bat-outing is already in the pipeline and more are being planned).

In addition, rumours began circulating that Leonardo was set for lead duties in a new biopic about James Dean, a troubled project which swung between directors for quite some time. In between all the production troubles, Leonardo eventually turned down the opportunity to star because he admitted 'I felt I wasn't experienced enough to play the part.' To this day, the movie remains uncast and no filming date has been set.

What Leonardo may have lacked in paycheques, however, he more than made up for

Leonardo's spectacular acting abilities branch out yet again

with a whole clutch of artistically satisfying projects, all of which had one thing in common; they all played upon the reputation he was gaining after *This Boy's Life* and *What's Eating Gilbert Grape?* for playing tortured, rebellious young things. It may have been an image at odds with his laid-back, happy life offscreen, but it was one he was seemingly more than happy to nurture in front of the camera.

Over the course of the next 18 months, he would gain attention from more than just the film reviewing press, becoming something of a gossip column staple in spite of his best attempts to keep his private life just that. The moviegoing millions, on the other hand would get to see him play the part of a tormented, drug addicted teenage poet in 20th Century America, a similarly unhappy, substance fuelled verse-scribbler in 18th Century France, and a reckless, rebellious gunslinger whose far from torturous existence would involve an onscreen kiss-up with Sharon Stone.

Leonardo at the 1994 Golden Globes with his Mum, Irmelin

4

Guns, Girls and Drugs

Leonardo takes on a trio of thoroughly diverse roles

Leonardo landed yet another legendary onscreen dad – Gene Hackman

Opposite: Leonardo gave the other gunslingers a run for their money – but proved no match for Sharon Stone

The Quick And The Dead, while not exactly a straightforward blockbuster, was the closest that Leonardo had yet come to appearing in a commercial project, largely due to the fact that he would be co-starring alongside the likes of Sharon Stone and Gene Hackman. In fact, it was entirely down to Sharon that he landed the role in the film at all, with the *Basic Instinct* siren having been so impressed by his previous work that she personally hand-picked him for the role of The Kid in the offbeat Western.

Directed by Sam Raimi, previously best known for such notorious horror flicks as *The Evil Dead*, *The Quick And The Dead* stars Sharon as a mysterious woman coming to a no-name town to seek revenge (for what, exactly, gradually becomes clear throughout the course of the movie) through a series of gun battles which involve her knocking off the majority of the grizzled stetson-wearers in the

Leonardo looking his coolest in *The Quick And The Dead*

town. Eventually the duels come to rest with a trio of figures – sheriff Herod (Gene Hackman), who obviously knows more about the woman than he's letting on, the man she has unexpectedly fallen for (played by Australian actor Russell Crowe) and The Kid, Herod's son, who is so keen to impress his grizzled father that he pretends to be far more of a gunslinging hero than he actually is.

Leonardo gets to enjoy himself enormously in the role, as a teenager basking in bravado, who can't wait to beat Sharon at her own game and spends most of the film talking about his prowess with a gun and messing around with bigger and bigger weapons. Unsurprisingly, most of it is just talk, and come the inevitable showdown with Sharon, it's a very different story. By this time, though, Leonardo has won over the audience by being the only character, aside from the leading lady, with a shred of humanity, although given the huge amount of comic book violence going on left, right and centre, it's impossible to take anybody too seriously.

This was, for the most part, the closest Leonardo had come to a comic performance – the movie was very humorous in tone and gave him the chance to swagger around talking tough in hugely impressive fashion while still retaining the mixed-up young man characteristics that had seen him through his career thus far. It did, in short, prove his versatility, at the same time equipping him with such fresh skills as horse-riding. On a more personal level, the media had begun to sit up and take notice of Leonardo, with his name beginning to creep around the gossip columns. Sharon Stone's admiration for the young actor proved so public that the pair were, naturally, romantically linked, rumours which proved to be unfounded. As it happens, the closest the pair did come to locking lips was sharing an onscreen kiss, and he was less than enamoured. 'It wasn't that great actually,' he later said of having to pucker up to his co-star. 'She grabbed me by the hair and pushed her lips against mine and then threw my head away. It was by no means a real kiss.'

Real or otherwise, it did nothing to help the box office performance of the film, which was released in the States the Autumn of 1994 to decidedly negative reviews and vanished from cinemas very quickly. The bizarre on-screen goings-on fared far better outside of the US, although Leonardo emerged from proceedings relatively unscathed, having garnered his fair share of acclaim on both sides of the Atlantic and was seen by many as the high point of the film. While his credibility was still intact, the all-important box office hit was still proving elusive.

Nor was it to prove forthcoming with his next batch of projects. Before embarking upon what would be his most intense role to date, Leonardo made a tiny appearance in a little-seen French production, *Une Cent Et Une Nuits* (One Hundred And One Nights). Billed only on the credits as Furtive And Friendly Appearance – Leonardo DiCaprio, the film itself centred on an ailing 100-year-old man whose nurse eases his suffering by telling him stories about all the movies ever made, while a bunch of student movie makers try to sponge cash off the centenarian for their own film-producing ends. Fellow Furtive and Friendly cameos came from the likes of

teen star Stephen Dorff and Gallic mega-star Gerard Depardieu, and an entire galaxy of stars, including Harrison Ford and Emily Lloyd, turn up under alternate guises. Given that the film was more of an ensemble piece featuring tiny cameos from all the above talent, Leonardo's appearance never attracted a great deal of attention.

Equally bizarre was a low-budget short film, *The Foot Shooting Party*, which saw Leonardo as a rock star being drafted for war. A black and white effort, it was most notable for the fact that it featured the man himself sporting hair extensions, although it still drifted by largely unnoticed, so much so that most people don't even realise Leonardo starred in it.

However, the same could not be said of his next outing, *The Basketball Diaries*. Based on the life of teen poet Jim Carroll, whose fondness for shooting hoops was nothing compared to his love of shooting heroin, the role required an actor who would be able to go from being the fresh face of the school basketball team, experimenting with drugs out of teenage curiosity, through a drug-hungry addict disowned by his mother and living in a filthy squat, through to, ultimately, a horrifying

L–R, Mark Wahlberg, Leonardo and James Hadid starring in *The Basketball Diaries*

Leonardo with sultry *Basketball Diaries* co-star Brittany Daniel

Leonardo and Mark Wahlberg at *The Basketball Diaries* premiere

and deeply unpleasant withdrawal scene. Until Leonardo came along, the project had been lingering on the shelf for some time, because the producers had been unable to find an actor who would be able to convey such a wide range of emotions so powerfully. However, once he appeared on the scene, they knew they had found their Jim Carroll.

The Basketball Diaries is, as might be expected, a grim movie experience which, while fascinating, is devoid of any humour or respite and as such hardly makes for a cosy night's viewing. But Leonardo's performance saves the day, whether he is scribbling poetry, having one of many conflicts with his onscreen mother (Lorraine Bracco) or indulging in an almighty drug-taking session with his friends. The film also marked the first major screen appearance of Mark Wahlberg (aka former pop star Marky Mark) who does an impressive job as Jim's sleazy best friend, the one responsible for his addiction in the first place.

Making the movie proved to be no easy task. While Leonardo's life long love of basketball (it is his favourite sport) stood him in good stead for the hoop-shooting scenes, the onscreen drug activity proved to be a different story. He spent several weeks prepping himself for the pivotal withdrawal scene and afterwards said of the experience 'it required me to achieve a primal state of being – I had to turn into an animal almost.' The results speak

for themselves, with Leonardo turning in an astoundingly convincing performance in the scene in question. 'I don't like what drugs do,' he later confessed. 'I don't do anything except drink once in a while.'

But what really brought him to public attention was his behaviour off-set. While shooting *The Basketball Diaries* in New York, Leonardo was rarely out of the tabloids for long thanks to his party animal activities, having been spotted at some of the Big Apple's hottest nightclubs on a number of occasions, with a string of different women, from actress Juliette Lewis (who appeared with Leonardo in *What's Eating Gilbert Grape?*) through to *Clueless* starlet Alicia Silverstone and teen supermodel Bridget Hall (best known for her modelling contract with designer Ralph Lauren).

As well as all the obvious romantic links, he was even linked to a couple of brawls in the aforementioned clubs. But while Leonardo admits he would much rather go out and party than remain 'cooped up in his hotel room', he is the first to point out that the majority of the reports were worryingly over-exaggerated, and that the fights were very much a figment of the tabloids' imagination. 'Bridget and I hung out for all of a week,' he later pointed out, 'the whole thing was totally blown out of proportion.'

The Basketball Diaries, on the other hand, didn't get quite the same amount of publicity, and despite Leonardo's performance getting the usual raves, the movie proved just too dark for mainstream cinema audiences and consequently went the way of all his other cinema outings. It performed marginally better outside of the US, although the British video release was marred due to a scene in which Jim Carroll dreams that he goes into his classroom with a shotgun and massacres his fellow pupils. As the small screen release was due just a couple of weeks after the Dunblane tragedy, the offending footage was appropriately removed.

Leonardo's next foray into the film world was an equally gloomy affair. *Total Eclipse* was a biopic based around the precocious 18th Century French poet Rimbaud, whose musings about life came to a swift end when he died at the age of 19. The crux of the film was his homosexual relationship with fellow verse-scribbler Verlaine (played by British actor David Thewlis), and the wild, largely opium-fuelled lifestyle that the pair of them led.

It seemed ironic that Leonardo should play two poets in a row, given that he is something of a scribe himself, and spends much of his offscreen time writing his own verse. Even more coincidentally, the part, which was originally meant to be taken by River Phoenix (with John Malkovich as Verlaine) became his after the former's tragic death. It was not the first time that Leonardo had gone up for a part vacated by River, as he was all set to play the crucial journalist hearing out Brad Pitt's 200-year-old tale in *Interview With The Vampire* –

Leonardo is re-united with Sharon Stone at the 1995 Oscars

Guns, Girls and Drugs

until that was bagged by Christian Slater. This time around, he was luckier. Jim Carroll, the writer he had played in *The Basketball Diaries*, actually suggested that he audition for Rimbaud, and it marked a major departure for Leonardo – not only did the script call for him to play a homosexual love scene, but also for him to appear nude, something he had never done before. Typically, he was entirely unfazed by it all, joking about the scene in question, in particular his judicious use of mouthwash beforehand.

Unfortunately, the film was his most poorly received yet, not even getting a theatrical release in some countries until two years after it was completed. Leonardo did, as usual, escape relatively unscathed, but many critics found the movie just too pretentious and dull for their liking, and unsurprisingly, the public stayed away.

Had Leonardo taken the *Batman Forever* route, he would no doubt have become a superstar by this point. But the fringe benefits of film stardom soon became apparent. He moved out of his mother's home into a swanky Los Angeles pad, which he now shares with his bizarre pet, a bearded dragon lizard, and a music collection that ranges from Pink Floyd to The Beatles and Led Zeppelin (he is also a big fan of rap music). He swapped his former set of wheels for a silver BMW Coupe. And, he began to find that despite the lack of box office success, he was able to pick and choose just whatever scripts came landing on his doormat.

Fortunately, Leonardo's next choice was not only a classic story, but finally provided him with that long-awaited box office smash. With period drama very much in vogue, thanks to the successful adaptation of Jane Austen's novels for the big screen, it seemed that the next writer to be dusted down and revived was Shakespeare – and with *Richard III* and Kenneth Branagh's four-hour *Hamlet* already on their way, it would only be a matter of time before the world's most timeless tale of star-crossed lovers followed them back into cinemas. *Romeo And Juliet* had been filmed before, it was true – but never quite like this. And if anybody had any doubts that Leonardo DiCaprio was heading for star status, this particular effort would change their minds.

Leonardo, David Thewlis and some fetching period costumes in *Total Eclipse*

20th Century Romeo

5

Shakespeare gets a shake-up and Leonardo gets a hit movie

Leonardo DiCaprio is a self-confessed romantic. 'When I'm alone with a girl, I can really get into the whole baby voices, rubbing noses – the teddy bear thing.' He has fond memories of his first date, with a girl named Cessi, who he spent the entire summer falling in love with over a series of lengthy phone conversations. 'Then she came home, and we met to go out for the first time, to the movies (the film in question being *When Harry Met Sally*). When I saw her I was so petrified I couldn't even look her in the eye.' Inevitably, the date went so disastrously wrong that the girl he had once been so keen on avoided him for months afterwards.

However, all of this stood him in good stead when he opted to play one half of the most famous romantic couple in the whole of literary history – the innocent lovestruck teenager Romeo in *William Shakespeare's Romeo And Juliet*, a role which required him to be both passionate and struck dumb at the sight of his first love. The adaptation in question promised to be quite unlike any screen version of the play so far – the last production, filmed in 1969 before Leonardo had even been born, was a largely traditional affair.

In the hands of Australian helmer Baz Luhrmann, on the other hand, it was a different story. The director, whose last film had been the wildly original comedy *Strictly Ballroom*, went for a thoroughly modern spin on things. The story – together with most of

Romeo And Juliet turned Leonardo's name into a household one

Opposite: *Romeo And Juliet* had critics everywhere in raptures

43

20th Century Romeo

the dialogue – has remained intact. Romeo and Juliet, for the uninitiated, are a pair of star-crossed lovers who fall head over heels for one another, even though their families are sworn enemies, woo each other from the latter's balcony, marry in secret and suffer the consequences when Romeo's best friend is killed and he ends up going on a vengeful spree that leads to him being banished from the town. Meanwhile, Juliet is being forced into a marriage she doesn't want to a nice but-oh-so-boring suitor, Paris, and is offered an escape method by a local priest so she can be with her new husband once again, but naturally it all goes horribly wrong and ends tragically.

What distinguished this particular *Romeo And Juliet*, however, was its setting. Originally taking place in the Italian city of Verona, the action now switches to the decidedly Los Angelean Verona Beach, with the opposing families taking the form of gangs who speed around in cars all day waging gun battles

against each other. Mercutio, the doomed best friend of Romeo, makes his initial appearance in a sequinned bra and hotpants number, and when Romeo and Juliet meet for the first time, they glimpse each other through a giant tank full of tropical fish. All this against a fantastic soundtrack featuring the likes of Garbage and The Cardigans, and an ending far more heartbreaking than any adaptation which has gone before it.

It seemed, in a way, that the part of Romeo could have been written for Leonardo, so perfect was he as the lovelorn one. As per usual, he seemed very much to play up the tortured young man side of things – when we first meet him, he is wandering the beach lamenting an unrequited love and looking thoroughly sorry for himself. Initially, he was reluctant to help bring the oft-filmed story to the screen yet again. 'My instinctive reaction was why do another one? There didn't seem to be a reason.' However, once he had travelled to Australia to meet with Baz Luhrmann, and

Leonardo, as Romeo, avenges the death of best friend Mercutio

20th Century Romeo

found out about the new interpretation for himself, his mind was soon changed. 'I realised it was a little more hard-core and a lot cooler,' he said afterwards. 'I certainly wouldn't have done it if I'd had to jump around in tights. But Baz Luhrmann heightened a lot of things in the story, made it kind of a futuristic fantasy world that made it a lot easier for people around my age to identify with the story. It wasn't just about *Romeo And Juliet* any more.'

The female half of the smitten couple, meanwhile, was played by young actress Claire Danes, an up-and-coming star who, like Leonardo, has been hailed as the finest new talent of her generation. At just 17, she has already accumulated roles in a whole host of movies with some of Hollywood's biggest names, starring as Winona Ryder's sickly sister in *Little Women*, playing Holly Hunter's daughter in *Home For The Holidays* and having the ghost of Michelle Pfeiffer as her mother in *To Gillian On Her 37th Birthday*. However, Claire is to date best known as

philosophical teen Angela Chase on the hugely popular TV series *My So-Called Life*, which has also brought her co-star Jared Leto to the attention of an adoring public. Amazingly, some people thought that Leonardo looked younger than his elfin co-star, despite the fact that he is five years her senior (she was 16, he 21 at the time of filming). But his boyish looks have always been an advantage for Leonardo, allowing him to play characters many years younger than himself and give them added depth thanks to his experience. Rounding out the cast were Hispanic actor John Leguizamo (best known for *Super Mario Brothers* and *To Wong Foo*), and British thesps Pete Postlethwaite and Miriam Margolyes.

Filming, meanwhile, entailed an arduous three-month stint in Mexico City, a place which the cast and crew found was frequently fraught with danger. While in South America, Leonardo cemented his status as a party animal once and for all, heading the cast in local parties, late-night board game sessions in

It can only be a matter of time before it all turns tragic

Leonardo hangs out with *Romeo And Juliet* director Baz Luhrmann

his hotel room and, on more than one occasion, checking out the nearby nightclubs. On one particularly bizarre night, things turned sour as one of Leonardo's friends, visiting from LA, was beaten up by a nightclub bouncer in an apparently motiveless attack, while trying to get into the club that his famous friend was already in. Across town, even weirder goings-on were afoot, as one of the film's crew members, upon hailing a taxi to return home from another club, was involved in a violent car-jacking that resulted in him being kidnapped, robbed and ultimately hospitalized. 'Loads of crazy things happened out there,' Leonardo later recalled. 'Four people (not involved with the film) from our hotel got murdered.'

And as if that wasn't enough, illness reared its head as well, with Leonardo, Claire and director Baz Luhrmann all going down with Montezuma's Revenge (a form of dysentery) which put them all out of action for at least a week. None of this, however, put paid to the star's natural exuberance which, as ever, shone through on set. Between takes he would bide his time running circuits of the set, dancing around to his beloved hip-hop music, doing Michael Jackson impersonations, and interspersing them with similar take-offs of cast members just as they strode in front of the camera to do their bit. In short, he was very much the centre of attention, not least from the local girls who came down to watch the shoot. But once he was called on set to do his bit, he had no trouble behaving himself and delivering the goods. And his disruptive behaviour is shrugged off by most of the directors he has worked with as part of his creative process. Leonardo is quick to explain: 'I would have a nervous breakdown if I had to be a character for three months on and off set. I know what I'm doing, but when they say Cut, I'm fine. I don't hide in a corner and yell at anyone who tries to speak to me. I don't want to become a strange person, or give up the life I already have.'

Nor, for that matter, did Leonardo appear phased by the goings on in Mexico City. 'It was an extraordinary place,' he says, 'We had fantastic places to use, the churches, the backdrops and the people added to the elements we wanted to use in the movie. But I think that being in a place like that, which was really dangerous – the actors kind of stuck around each other and developed a good tight bond.'

Romeo And Juliet; don't try this one at home

That first meeting; Leonardo as Romeo peeps through the fish tank and claps eyes on Juliet

Something which did, of course, spark off the inevitable rumours that Leonardo and Claire had become romantically entwined for real during the shoot, especially given the astonishing onscreen chemistry which set reports had suggested they were generating. However, such allegations were swiftly scotched, with him laying claim to a non-showbiz girlfriend whom he had been dating for some time, and her long-term involvement with rock musician Andrew Dorff, younger brother of *Backbeat* star Stephen. (The pair have since parted company). In fact, there were times, especially towards the end of filming, when things became quite fraught between the two of them. But after the numerous traumas they had experienced together, by the end the pair had formed a close bond, and were behaving like brother and sister.

Romeo And Juliet, meanwhile, made its debut US outing on November 1, 1996, following an energetic summer which had seen Leonardo trying his hand at the riskiest white knuckle sports going – white water rafting,

bungee jumping and even a parachute jump. The first two were just fine, but the skydiving nearly ended in disaster after the star's parachute failed to open, leaving him free-falling thousands of feet until the backup chute was able to inflate. Far safer, if no less scary, was the second leg of the vacation, which saw him taking in some of Los Angeles's best theme parks – he claims to have visited Knott's Berry Farm, Magic Mountain, Raging Waters and Universal Studios three times each in the space of only a couple of months.

His next public appearance was at the American premiere of *Romeo And Juliet*, at which he revealed just where his romantic interests lay, showing up arm-in-arm with model Kristin Zang. Although Leonardo is renowned for keeping his private life private, it soon became apparent that the pair had already been an item for around a year. Indeed, Leonardo's fondness for fashion shows is one of the reasons why he has become such a tabloid favourite over the past couple of years.

Most notably, *Romeo And Juliet* helped to drag Leonardo out of his undeserved box office slump. Against some fantastic reviews, the film shot to the top of the US box office, making over $14 million in its first weekend on release and bringing Shakespeare to audiences who had never previously considered it. In particular, the film reached a large teenage audience, who lapped up its young, sexy, MTV-style approach to its subject matter. In the end, the film grossed around $50 million in the US and was a similar success in other parts of the world.

Even more importantly, *Romeo And Juliet* established its leading man as a force to be reckoned with. Many talked of a second Oscar nomination for Leonardo, but when Academy Awards time rolled around, the film was mentioned only in the technical categories. This didn't stop it snagging its much deserved acclaim elsewhere though, and at the Berlin Film Festival the following February Leonardo was the proud recipient of the Silver Bear Award for Best Actor for that very film. What's more, *Romeo And Juliet* was not overlooked when the MTV Movie Awards rolled around either, with the film copping six nominations, including Best

Male Performance for Leonardo and Best Female Performance for Claire Danes, as well as Best Fight Sequence and Best Movie, which pitted it against such stiff competition as *Scream* and *Independence Day*.

By now, there can have been absolutely no doubt in anybody's mind that Leonardo DiCaprio had arrived. His acting talents were up there on screen for all to see, his face adorned many a teenager's wall and, to top it all off nicely, he finally had a hit film in the bag. He even began building his mother a home in West Virginia, far away from the sleazy Hollywood suburb where he had grown up. But rather than capitalise on the success of *Romeo And Juliet*, his next film saw him returning to the low-key affairs of old, a movie which not only re-united him with Robert De Niro but also allowed him to work with the likes of Diane Keaton and Meryl Streep. It was merely a temporary move, however, for it was only going to be a matter of months before he found himself taking the lead in one of the most expensive movies ever to go before a camera. The film in question was James Cameron's *Titanic*, and the hype machine had been set in motion before a reel of film had even been shot.

Romeo and Mercutio (Harold Perrineau) gear up for another battle

The women in Leonardo's life; Mother Irmelin and model girlfriend Kristen Zang

6

Maiden Voyage

Next, Leonardo DiCaprio set sail for stardom aboard the biggest film of all time, *Titanic*

The success of *Romeo And Juliet* firmly established Leonardo DiCaprio as one of Hollywood's hottest properties. After years of playing offbeat roles in unconventional projects, Leonardo traded cult status for minor stardom thanks to Baz Luhrmann's super-stylish Shakespeare showcase. The actor's powerhouse performance, coupled with his exotic good looks and irresistible charm, swiftly captured the hearts and minds of teenagers around the world. Perhaps more importantly, though, *Romeo And Juliet* had demonstrated Leonardo's ability to topline a major production with mass appeal. This lesson certainly wasn't wasted on industry moguls, who fully expected Leonardo to follow *Romeo And Juliet* with a blockbuster designed to take the 21-year-old talent into the hallowed Hollywood 'A' list of film superstars.

Leonardo's career would, of course, enter the stratosphere with *Titanic*. But before he set sail with the epic romantic drama, the actor once again stunned Hollywood by choosing a low-budget, ensemble piece as his follow-up to *Romeo And Juliet*. Based on a popular off-Broadway play, *Marvin's Room* focuses on two estranged sisters, Lee and Bessie (played by Academy Award winners Meryl Streep and Diane Keaton), who are forced to reconcile their differences when the latter is diagnosed with leukaemia.

In addition to Streep and Keaton, the film's all-star cast includes Hume Cronyn, Gwen Verdon, and Robert De Niro. Leonardo and Hal Scardino round-up this heavyweight line-up as Lee's two troubled teenage sons, Hank and Charlie. Between them, the cast of *Marvin's Room* had garnered five Academy Awards and a further 19 nominations, one of which belonged to Leonardo for *What's Eating Gilbert Grape?*

Although in many ways the role of Hank seemed tailor-made for Leonardo, his management advised him against playing yet another disturbed teenager and suggested that he held out for a more mainstream, star-driven project. On this particular issue, however, Leonardo firmly dismissed their advice. Ever since he had read the script for *Marvin's Room* during the making of *This Boy's Life* in 1992, the actor had set his heart on appearing in the film.

Right from the start, Leonardo had no misconceptions about his role in *Marvin's Room*. He fully understood that the film was an ensemble piece, which largely revolved around its two female leads. As far as he was concerned, the main attraction of the project was that he would be working with legendary talents like Meryl Streep, for whom he later declared his 'complete respect'.

Nevertheless, the young actor still claimed some of the most memorable moments in *Marvin's Room* – as well as second billing in the film's credits. Predictably, Leonardo was both compelling and utterly convincing as a troubled teen with a heart of gold. His performance subsequently earned him a Golden Samovar Award at the Moscow Film Festival as well as a nomination for Outstanding Performance at the Screen Actors' Guild Awards.

Despite its cast's best efforts, *Marvin's Room* ultimately emerged as a low-key and lacklustre melodrama, which earned lukewarm reviews at best. Fortunately, the production still managed to turn a tidy profit, giving Leonardo his second consecutive hit.

Having defied all Hollywood conventions by following *Romeo And Juliet* with *Marvin's Room*, few dared speculate on what Leonardo's next project would be. If anything, it seemed likely that he would continue his long-standing love affair with arthouse movie-making and lend his name to another offbeat project. Instead,

Opposite: Yet another disturbed teen role for Leonardo, this time as Meryl Streep's son in *Marvin's Room*

RYL STREEP   LEONARDO DiCAPRIO   DIANE KEATON   and   ROBERT DE NIRO

A story about the years
that keep us apart...
And the moments
that bring us together.

MARVIN'S
ROOM

MIRAMAX FILMS PRESENTS A SCOTT RUDIN/TRIBECA PRODUCTION   MERYL STREEP   LEONARDO DiCAPRIO   DIANE KEATON   ROBERT DE NIRO   HUME CRONYN   GWEN VERDON
MARVIN'S ROOM   HAL SCARDINO   JULIE WEISS   RACHEL PORTMAN   JIM CLARK   DAVID GROPMAN   PIOTR SOBOCINSKI
DAVID WISNIEVITZ   ADAM SCHROEDER   SCOTT McPHERSON   SCOTT RUDIN   JANE ROSENTHAL   ROBERT DE NIRO   JERRY ZAKS

MIRAMAX

however, the actor was actually destined to play the most accessible role of his career in the biggest film of all time. The film was called *Titanic*, and would thrust Leonardo into the spotlight as never before.

Titanic was the brainchild of its writer-producer-director, James Cameron (*True Lies*, *Terminator*). Cameron first came up with the idea of making a movie about the doomed ocean liner in 1985, while watching Robert Ballard's real life footage of the shipwreck at the bottom of the Atlantic. A subsequent viewing of the classic 1958 Titanic film *A Night To Remember* provided further fuel for the director's passion, and inspired him to write a 167 page treatment for the project.

Cameron's story follows the launch of the 'unsinkable' H.M.S. *Titanic* and its subsequent destruction on April 14 1912 through the eyes of two unlikely young lovers: the headstrong aristocrat Rose DeWitt Bukater; and free-spirited artist Jack Dawson. After Jack prevents Rose from committing suicide, the pair fall in love and ultimately face the Titanic's destruction together.

When Cameron approached Fox with *Titanic* in March 1995, he faced a surprisingly tepid reaction. Studio chiefs pointed out that the ship had already featured in a number of films and telemovies, and felt that the subject matter no longer held much appeal. However, Fox initially agreed to finance the project to the tune of $80 million – $3 million of which was earmarked to shoot footage of the actual wreck.

Casting began towards the end of 1995. To keep costs to a minimum, Cameron decided that two rising stars – rather than established A-list actors – would play *Titanic*'s doomed lovers. Fox's first choice for the role of Jack was Matthew McConaughey (A *Time To Kill*, *Contact*), with Chris O'Donnell (*Batman Forever*) a close second. Cameron, however, dismissed these suggestions and sought a male lead who could convincingly play Jack as a 17-year-old.

As the search continued, casting director Mali Finn suggested that Cameron should meet *Romeo And Juliet*'s Leonardo DiCaprio. Cameron was initially unimpressed, as he felt that Leonardo wasn't conventional leading

Jack Dawson (Leonardo) shows the lovely Rose DeWitt Bukater (played by Kate Winslett) his portfolio on A-deck in the mega-movie *Titanic*

Yet another legendary co-star for Leonardo – this time Diane Keaton in *Marvin's Room*

man material. Nonetheless, he did agree to meet the actor to discuss the project. And from the second Leonardo read for the role, Cameron could see that he would be perfect as Jack. Not only could the 21-year-old actor easily pass as a 17-year-old, but he was also someone who the audience care for.

'He has tremendous vitality on screen,' Cameron later said. 'Leo has a kind of wiry survival quality about him that's pretty cool.'

Much to Cameron and Fox's surprise, though, Leonardo was reluctant to commit himself to *Titanic*. Following the completion of *Marvin's Room*, the actor had been courted by the producers of a diverse range of interesting projects. These included Francis Ford Coppola's legal thriller *The Rainmaker*, the low-budget drama *Boogie Nights* and the ambitious character study *The Minds of Billy Milligan*.

It was only after a great deal of soul searching, then, that Leonardo accepted Fox's $1 million offer to board *Titanic* in June 1996. Ironically, it wasn't the idea of starring in a blockbuster or consolidating his star status that appealed to the actor. Instead, the main attraction of *Titanic* for Leonardo was its central love story and the chance to play its hero, Jack.

'Jack is a sort of wandering person who seizes on the opportunities life presents to him,' Leonardo said of his character. 'At a young age, I think he realizes how short life really is, and that's a big factor in who he is as a person.'

Leonardo was joined at the top of *Titanic*'s Call Sheet by British actress Kate Winslet. Best known for her Academy Award-nominated turn in *Sense & Sensibility*, Kate fought off stiff competition from the likes of Gwyneth Paltrow (*Shakespeare In Love*), Gabrielle Anwar (*The Concierge*) and *Romeo And Juliet*'s Claire Danes to claim the role of Rose DeWitt Bukater.

With its doomed lovers in place, *Titanic* began shooting in July 1996. By that time, the film's budget had already risen to $110 million and that wasn't the last price hike the production would experience. Filming commenced on location in Halifax, Nova Scotia, where the movie's modern day sequences featuring *Twister*'s Bill Paxton as treasure hunter Brock Lovett were shot. Lovett's discovery of a famous gem among the debris of the Titanic leads him to a 100-year-old Rose (played by Gloria Swanson), who offers her account of the ship's demise.

Leonardo in *Marvin's Room* with co-star Meryl Streep as his hairdresser Mum

While shooting in Nova Scotia, *Titanic* suffered the first of many setbacks. In a mystery worthy of any movie, the cast and crew's food was poisoned with the hallucinogenic drug Phecyclidine (also known as PCP or 'Angel Dust'). 80 people were taken ill, including Cameron and Bill Paxton.

In September, filming relocated to Baja, Mexico, where a 90% replica of the H.M.S. *Titanic* awaited. Measuring 750 feet and weighing 1.3 million tonnes, the $40 million set had been built inside a 17 million gallon water tank, to give the impression that it was at sea.

September 20 marked Leonardo's first day of filming. And it was a baptism of fire for the young actor, as he was immediately required to shoot the scene in which Jack paints Rose – in the nude. To ease the tension on-set, Kate Winslet shocked her co-star by flashing at him! Her actions certainly broke the ice, and the screen couple soon formed a close – and firmly platonic – friendship in real life.

'I think she's such a terrific girl,' Leonardo later said of Winslet on *Good Morning America*. 'We were such good friends throughout this whole movie.'

Winslet was equally complimentary of her co-star and revealed that they swapped bedroom secrets to pass the time on-set!

For Leonardo, the biggest challenge of working on *Titanic* was making sure that his character suited the era. To this end, he studied everything from speech to the art of holding a fork with dialect coach Susan Hegart and choreographer/etiquette coach Lynne Hockney. Ironically, though, he would ultimately ignore many of their suggestions.

'I worked with the etiquette coach,' Leonardo explained, 'and halfway into it, I realized that in order to make Jack the character he is, he sort of needs to ignore such things. I'm supposed to stick out like a sore thumb in these environments.'

By all accounts, *Titanic* was an exceptionally difficult shoot. Ever the perfectionist, Cameron would accept nothing but the best from the film's cast and crew, who were required to work 19 hour days. Predictably, the most gruelling scenes for Leonardo and Winslet proved to be the film's waterlogged sequences. At one point, Kate Winslet almost drowned when her costume dragged her beneath water.

Titanic finally wrapped on March 22 1997, with the completion of a kiss between Jack and Rose. Filming finished two months late, by which time *Titanic*'s budget had soared to a staggering $200 million, making it the most expensive movie of all time.

Following all the film's production problems, Fox's announcement that *Titanic* would miss its scheduled July 4 release day represented another major setback. And the subsequent revelation that the movie needed to earn $500 million at the box office just to break even was widely seen as the final nail in the film's coffin. When the movie's American premiere was set for Christmas, it seemed that Cameron planned to mark the holiday season by presenting cinemagoers with a $200 million turkey.

Fortunately, in the run-up to December 1997, the tide slowly began to turn. The first test screening of *Titanic* in August was an overwhelming success, as the audience savoured every second of Cameron's epic three hour, 14 minute cut. The following month, a five minute trailer for the movie became a cinema attraction in its own right.

The reaction to the trailer was, of course, just to the tip of the iceberg. Following its Stateside launch in December 1997, *Titanic* confounded all expectations by becoming the highest-grossing movie of all time. It stayed at the top of the American box office for a record 26 weeks, and was the first film to earn over $1 billion worldwide. *Titanic*'s final tally would settle at $1.2 billion.

Despite a mixed critical reaction, *Titanic* was embraced without reservation by cinemagoers around the world. The film's deft blend of romance, drama and sumptuous visuals drew obvious comparison with the likes of *Gone With The Wind* and *Dr Zhivago*. And the power of Cameron's vision was undeniable.

Titanic's strengths weren't overlooked by America's leading award ceremonies. The film was nominated for eight Golden Globes (including one for Leonardo), of which it collected Best Picture, Best Director, Best Score and Best Song. It also figured in 14 Academy Award categories, and subsequently collected 11 gongs, including Best Picture and Best Director.

While the film's 11 Oscar wins matched the all-time record set by *Ben Hur*, its historic

Jack (Leonardo) joins Rose (Kate Winslet) for dinner as a reward for 'saving her life' in a scene from *Titanic*

Titanic's stars worked 19 hours a day in often gruelling conditions to capture director James Cameron's unique vision of the legendary ocean liner's destruction

Leonardo's arrival at the 1998 Golden Globe Awards was greeted by shrieks of joy from thousands of adoring fans – the trademark of the new global phenomenon known as 'Leomania'

achievement was eclipsed by the Academy's failure to even nominate Leonardo for an Award. The Academy's controversial decision made the headlines, as did Leonardo's absence from the ceremony. Although some reports speculated that Leonardo deliberately spurned the event, the actor insisted that he simply didn't want to upstage his nominated colleagues.

And had he attended, Leonardo would probably have done just that. Because of everyone who worked on Titanic, Leonardo DiCaprio was the biggest benefactor. This was evident from the movie's premiere at the Tokyo Film Festival on November 1 1997, which was attended by Leonardo and James Cameron. Upon arriving at the Festival, the pair were greeted by thousands of screaming fans, all of whom had come to see Titanic's leading man. The turnout was so incredible that it officially gave birth to the term, 'Leomania'.

Leomania was also the dominant force at the 1998 Blockbuster Awards. After claiming the prizes for Favorite Actor (Drama) and Best Male Actor (Drama) as well as the American Moviegoer Award for Best Actor (Drama), it was clear that the public didn't share the Academy's lack of regard for Leonardo. The

actor also found himself labelled one of 'The 50 Most Beautiful People In The World' by People magazine, named the 86th most powerful person in Hollywood by Premiere and dubbed 'Entertainer of the Year 1998' by Entertainment Weekly.

Inevitably, Leonardo also found his every move studied by the press in the wake of Leomania. The actor was romantically linked with everyone from Roseanne's Sara Gilbert and Clueless sensation Alicia Silverstone to former What's Eating Gilbert Grape? co-star Juliette Lewis and even Ghost's Demi Moore. And every detail of his long-running on-off relationship with model Kristen Zang became public knowledge.

Fortunately, Leonardo took everything in his stride. More than anything, he was simply amused and bemused by Leomania. And the experience of becoming the world's hottest heart-throb did little to affect his feelings about his star turn in Titanic.

'I was part of something that doesn't come about often, if ever,' he stated in Film Review. 'I can tell my grandchildren that I was in this film and became an icon. It became something that people identify with worldwide and that was the main honour of being part of the movie.'

7

Life's a beach

Titanic's major success gave DiCaprio the power to pick and choose projects

As soon as the final reel of Titanic finished unrolling, cinemageors around the world waited with bated breath to see where Leonardo DiCaprio would resurface. Fortunately, they wouldn't have too wait long at all. The lengthy post-production schedule of James Cameron's fantastic voyage meant that Leonardo's next film was in the can by the time Titanic had set sail. And the film boasted the unique attraction of starring Leonardo DiCaprio in not one but two roles!

Inspired by the classic Alexandre Dumas novel, *The Man In The Iron Mask* toplines Leonardo as both the evil King Louis XIV of France and Louis' long-lost twin brother, Philippe. Tired of the King's selfish behaviour, the aging Three Musketeers, Aramis (Jeremy Irons), Athos (John Malkovich) and Porthos (Gerard Depardieu) embark on a mission to free Philippe from prison and restore justice in their land.

The Man In The Iron Mask began its 14 week shoot on location in France on April 28 1997, only a few weeks after Leonardo had disembarked from *Titanic*. Having spent the best part of six months playing the carefree hero Jack Dawson, the twin lead roles in the swashbuckling 18th century costume drama proved simply irresistible for the actor. Besides allowing Leonardo to portray the evil tyrant, it also cast him as another tortured character –

The Man in The Iron Mask presented cinemagoers with two Leonardos for the price of one, as the actor played both the evil King Louis XIV and his tortured twin brother, Philippe

namely the king's brother Philippe, the eponymous man in the iron mask.

'The thing I found that was interesting when I talked to Randy [Wallace, director] about it,' the actor later explained to journalists, 'is that he saw Philippe as a Nelson Mandela-figure, who was trapped in a place for so long and did only good while he was enclosed by himself. Mandela came out and ended up ruling his country. The mind must take over the body and [Philippe is] able to control himself and not completely lose it, which I found very interesting.'

Although portraying two distinct characters in one film is never easy, Leonardo took it all in his stride. He was also completely unfazed by working with such heavyweight thespian talent as Jeremy Irons, Gerard Depardieu, John Malkovich and Gabriel Byrne.

'That was unbelievable, working with those guys,' Leonardo later said of his co-stars in the film during an interview on *Good Morning America*. 'I mean it's so cool working with people in that calibre because they're so relaxed about everything.'

The Man In The Iron Mask was launched Stateside on March 13 1998, while *Titanic* was still on general release. Consequently, Leonardo found himself as the star of America's two biggest films of the week, with his *Iron Mask* second only to his cruise aboard the *Titanic*.

Leonardo's take on the Dumas novel won decidedly mixed reviews, with most critics concluding that it added little to earlier adaptations of *The Man In The Iron Mask*. Some reviewers also felt that Leonardo's performance was disappointing, and claimed that his co-stars were better suited to the material than their young leading man. It was this line of thinking which earned Leonardo's work in the film a notorious Golden Raspberry Award for 'Worst Screen Couple' in 1999!

Yet while *The Man In The Iron Mask* wasn't Leonardo's finest hour, it remained entertaining costume fare and turned another tidy profit at the box office. And the actor's loyal fans certainly weren't disappointed by the chance to see their idol in dual roles – or with elegant hair extensions!

King Louis XIV's treacherous behaviour in *The Man in the Iron Mask* provided Leonardo with a welcome contrast from playing *Titanic*'s wholesome hero, Jack Dawson

Life's a Beach

Leonardo was next seen on the big screen towards the end of 1998, playing a cameo role in Woody Allen's *Celebrity*. Like *The Man In The Iron Mask*, *Celebrity* was actually shot before *Titanic* fever swept the world, although it did reap the benefits of Leomania.

Shot in black and white, Allen's satire on modern fame showcases an all-star cast which includes Kenneth Branagh, Judy Davis, Melanie Griffith, Famke Janssen, Joe Mantegna, Winona Ryder and Charlize Theron. Yet it was Leonardo's 12 minute appearance as heart-throb actor Brandon Darrow during the film's second half that gave *Celebrity* its pulling power. Tellingly, the actor featured on the film's poster and was the centre of attention during its premiere at the New York Film Festival in November 1998.

'I had a wonderful time working with Woody – a great director,' Leonardo told reporters at the premiere. 'Woody cast me because he liked my performance in *Marvin's Room*.'

Inevitably, Leonardo's role as a hellraising superstar led many to wonder if he was just playing himself in *Celebrity*. But such claims were happily refuted by his co-star, Kenneth Branagh. 'I find Leo very together and able to be funny about what's happened to him,' he explained in *Film Review*.

Following *Celebrity*, Leonardo lent his distinctive vocal style to a CD-Rom produced by Steven Spielberg's Shoah Foundation. *Survivors: Testimonies of the Holocaust* combines archival footage with survivors' accounts of what happened to them, and is narrated by Leonardo and Winona Ryder.

In Woody Allen's satirical comedy-drama, *Celebrity*, showbiz journalist and aspiring screenwriter Lee Simon (Kenneth Branagh) sees his friendship with heart-throb actor Brandon Darrow (Leonardo DiCaprio) as his ticket to the big time

While films like *Man In The Iron Mask* and *Celebrity* had helped feed the world's hunger for Leonardo, most cinemagoers were intrigued to see what would be his first true post-*Titanic* project. In true Leonardo style, the actor's response stunned the world.

'I'm taking a year off,' he announced in *The Daily Mirror*. 'I want to slow down because I've been working so hard ... [There are] so many things I've not had the chance to do just because of work.'

Leonardo immediately began his 'year-out' by embarking on a life of full-time party-going. And naturally, the press were with him every step of the way. Reports of Leonardo's rowdy antics became common-

place, and the actor found himself linked to the likes of Kate Moss, Naomi Campbell and *Showgirls* star Elizabeth Berkley.

During the summer of 1998, Leonardo hit the front page by taking legal action against *Playgirl* magazine, which planned to publish unauthorized nude photos of the actor. The case was ultimately settled out-of-court in Leonardo's favour.

Even more, headlines were made when Leonardo and his co-star, Tobey Maguire, were publicly accused of trying to prevent the release of *Don's Plum*. Filmed over six days in 1995 and 1996, the low-budget drama focuses on a group of friends who gather one night to discuss the darker aspects of life. This

Art imitates life in *Celebrity*, as Leonardo's screen counterpart faces hordes of adoring fans and intense media attention

71

Life's a Beach

group includes Leonardo, who played a drug-using womaniser as a favour to the film's director, R. D. Robb.

While Leonardo refused to comment on these charges, it was widely reported that the actor had been led to believe that *Don's Plum* would only be a short film, in the mould of *The Foot Shooting Party*. This would explain his objection to *Don's Plum* being turned into a full length feature for theatrical distribution.

Despite his decision to take a well-earned rest, Leonardo did continue to read scripts in 1998. He famously toyed with the idea of toplining the film adaptation of Brett Easton Ellis' controversial novel *American Psycho*, and the production company Lion's Gate was happy to rework the entire film to suit him. On hearing of Leonardo's interest, it promptly transformed the planned $5 million movie into a medium-budget star vehicle and then ignominiously dropped original writer-director Mary Harron along with her leading man, Christian Bale (*Velvet Goldmine*).

News of Leonardo's interest in playing a serial killer drew widespread criticism, with most commentators insisting that the actor was setting a bad example for his fans. Ultimately, though, *American Psycho* would not topline the *Titanic* star. After failing to attract Oliver Stone and Martin Scorcese to the project, Leonardo bowed out and *American Psycho* returned to its low budget roots with Mary Harron and Christian Bale.

Other projects which Leonardo considered during this period included the 1930s drama *I Lay Dying*, Spike Lee's *Summer of Sam*, the sweeping drama *The Laws of Madness* and the 1940s rites of passage tale *All The Pretty Horses*.

While all these projects piqued Leonardo's interest, the one which finally secured his participation was *The Beach*. Based on the 1991 novel written by Alex Garland, the film follows the adventures of a young traveller, Richard Lewis, who finds a map which supposedly leads to a legendary Thai island paradise. During the search for this haven, Richard becomes entangled in a love triangle with two female travellers.

The Beach was developed for the screen by the *Trainspotting* triumvirate of writer John Hodge, producer Andrew MacDonald and director Danny Boyle. Although Leonardo was

After toying with a number of diverse projects, Leonardo chose *The Beach* as his first true post-*Titanic* outing and began shooting the film on location in Thailand during January 1999

Life's a Beach

Despite *The Beach*'s exotic setting, Leonardo had little time to enjoy life in Thailand. Besides pursuing a gruelling work schedule, the actor also faced a heavily publicised local environmental protest

unfamiliar with the novel, he had long admired Boyle's work and was intrigued by the prospect of working on his latest project.

'I was a big fan of Danny Boyle before [*The Beach*] came about,' the actor told *The LA Times* in an interview. 'I saw the type of film-making he does as unique.'

Leonardo pipped longtime Boyle collaborator Ewan McGregor (*Star Wars: The Phantom Menace*) to the lead role in *The Beach*, and his involvement in the film transformed it into a $45 million production. As a sign of his growing status, a cool $20 million of the film's budget went to Leonardo, instantly making him one of Hollywood's top earners.

For his part, Boyle saw Leonardo's casting as a chance to play with the actor's *Titanic* persona as well as the preconceived notions of the audience. 'We're trying not to fulfil those expectations, but twist them round a bit,' said the director in *The Daily Telegraph*. 'I think that's what interested Leo in this film. There's a darkness at the end which is quite different from the sadness at the end of *Titanic*.'

While Leonardo's casting was officially announced on July 28 1998, he would not begin work on *The Beach* until January 1999. This gave him time to complete his one-year vacation from film-making, as well as to gain some muscle needed for the part.

Like *Titanic*, *The Beach* was hardly a smooth production. The movie was plagued with controversy from before the cameras even started rolling on location in Thailand. Upon learning that the film's crew were temporarily altering the landscape and shrubbery of Maya Beach on Phi Phi Le island, local environmentalists launched a vicious protest in October 1998. Donning masks of Leonardo, they marched to the Silom offices of 20th Century Fox and vehemently expressed their displeasure at the situation.

A long series of protests and law suits followed, much to the annoyance of local authorities who insisted that the producers of *The Beach* would not harm the environment. Agriculture Minister Pongpol Adireksarn also condemned the protester's methods, pointing out that Leonardo had nothing to do with the controversy whatsoever.

In any case, by the time Leonardo secretly flew into Thailand in January, he knew that he was heading for a storm. Startled by the enormity of the protest, the actor swiftly issued a public statement on the matter.

'I would never, by any means, intentionally go forth with a project that I believed would damage the environment of any country, or the image of Thailand,' insisted Leonardo. 'From what I see with my own eyes, everything is OK. I have seen nothing that had been destroyed or damaged in any way.'

Leonardo then pointed out that the film would ultimately be of great benefit to the local community. 'I think the release of a film like this will encourage young people to see the beauty of Thailand, and encourage more young backpackers to come here.'

In addition to the stress of the environmental protest, Leonardo also faced a gruelling work schedule on *The Beach*. He worked for 63 of the production's 67 shooting days, and left his hotel at 5:30am most mornings, seldom returning before 8pm.

'It's been incredible shooting on an island like this, but it's about work and more work,' Leonardo noted in a *Now* magazine article. 'My life is spent either on the boat or sleeping at the hotel.'

To make matters worse, Leonardo was stung by a jellyfish during filming, and spent

stung by a jellyfish during filming, and spent the best part of a day recovering. And then, in true *Titanic* style, the actor's boat was capsized by high waves, during a minor incident which made front pages around the world.

When principal photography of *The Beach* finally wrapped at the end of April, its cast and crew of breathed a collective sigh of relief. However, if the parallels with *Titanic* continue, their hard work will all be worthwhile. Judging by the talent of the Trainspotting triumvirate, the popularity of the source novel and the response to the film's teaser trailer, Leonardo

would seem to have another sizeable hit on his hands. And that fact that the actor spends most of his time in *The Beach* sans-shirt won't do its box office prospects any harm at all.

With *The Beach* behind him, Leonardo has a series of further projects lined up. First and foremost on this list is Martin Scorsese's *The Gangs of New York*. An epic tale of Irish gangsters which spans from the mid-1800s through to the 20th century, Scorsese's latest crime flick is slated to feature Leonardo alongside his familiar co-star, Robert De Niro.

Leonardo is also set to topline the long-

In the run-up to its premiere in December 1999, *The Beach* was widely tipped for box office glory – and some insiders even claimed that it would earn Leonardo the Academy Award nomination which had eluded him for *Titanic*

Life's a Beach

**From child star to A-list movie sensation,
Leonardo DiCaprio has taken fame and fortune
in his stride**

delayed thriller *Slay the Dreamer*. The film focuses on a young attorney's attempts to expose a conspiracy surrounding the assassination of the civil-rights leader Martin Luther King, and would also feature *Pulp Fiction*'s Samuel L. Jackson.

Other projects in the pipeline include the cold war drama *Bombshell: The Secret Story of America's Unknown Atomic Spy Conspiracy*, the 1970s thriller *Stanford Prison Experiment*, the Marlon Brando vehicle *One Arm*, the long-stalled James Dean biopic and an adaptation of Jack Kerouac's *On The Road*.

As if these films aren't enough to keep him busy for quite a long time, Leonardo is also reported to have optioned the movie rights to two further projects through his Birken Productions company. The first, *Dreamland*, chronicles the exploits of an Eastern European immigrant in turn-of-the-century New York City, while the second is a biopic of the legendary jazz trumpeter Chet Baker.

And then, of course, there are those wild rumours about Leonardo playing *Spiderman* or even Anakin Skywalker in the second and third *Star Wars* prequels. While many of his fans would love to see him in these roles, it's highly unlikely that Leonardo would be able to find the time to fit them into his hectic schedule. But then, as the actor himself has shown so often, anything is possible.

Clearly, the world is Leonardo's oyster. After proving his worth both as an actor and as a box office draw, the former child star now has the power to pick and choose projects as he pleases. And his interest alone is enough to get a movie made.

But despite his star power, adoring fans and an estimated fortune of $37 million, it seems that Leonardo remains unaffected by the trappings of fame. He continues to seek out projects solely on their artistic merit and pays little attention to their commercial viability. While he enjoys his showbiz parties, he's almost always accompanied by old friends from his pre-stardom days. And above all, he doesn't believe in his own hype.

Faced with that kind of no-lose scenario, Leonardo DiCaprio's career looks pretty unsinkable. Provided he continues to combine sterling performances with intriguing choices, the one-time 'King of the World' will remain King of cinemagoers' hearts and minds for decades to come.

FILM

TV

Selected Credits